KT-473-036

LEARNING TO HEAR

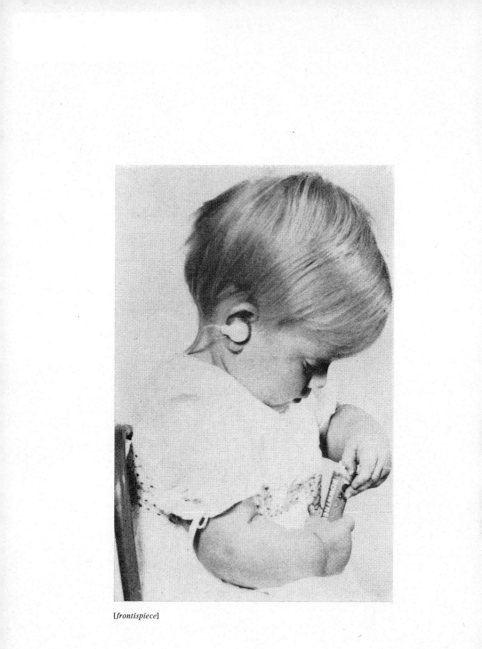

[*frontispiece*]

LEARNING TO HEAR

EDITH WHETNALL

M.S. (Lond.), F.R.C.S. (Eng.)

*Late Founder and first Director of
Nuffield Hearing and Speech Centre, formerly
Audiology Unit, Royal National Throat, Nose and Ear
Hospital; Late Consultant Aural Surgeon, School
Medical Service, London County Council*

AND

D. B. FRY

Ph.D. (Lond.)

*Professor of Experimental Phonetics in the University
of London; Consultant in Phonetics, Nuffield Hearing
and Speech Centre, Royal National Throat, Nose and
Ear Hospital*

Edited by

R. B. NIVEN, M.A., B.M., B.Ch. (Oxon),
M.A. (Cape Town), F.R.C.P. (London)

WILLIAM HEINEMANN · MEDICAL BOOKS · LIMITED
LONDON

First Published 1970

© R. B. Niven and D. B. Fry, 1970

S.B.N. 433 23250

Made in Great Britain at the Pitman Press, Bath

CONTENTS

CHAP.   PAGE

      Editor's Preface   vii

   I How it Began   1

  II The Ear and How it Works   10

 III We Hear with Our Brains   18

 IV Deaf but not Dumb   38

  V Facts of Physics   65

 VI Types and Causes of Deafness   84

 VII Detection of Deafness: Tests of Hearing   99

VIII Auditory Training   116

 IX Hearing Aids   123

      Epilogue   138

      Index   141

EDITOR'S PREFACE

A child is utterly dependent on the adults near to him, most of all on his mother and father. This is true for every child but most of all for the child with a handicap. The special help needed by the handicapped child cannot start until the disability has been detected. Edith Whetnall was sure that the best means of early detection of deafness was a well-informed public whose suspicions would be aroused by deviations from the normal in a child's development of hearing and speech.

With Professor D. B. Fry she had produced a Medical Monograph *The Deaf Child* which epitomised for professional readers their experience at the Audiology Unit (now the Nuffield Hearing and Speech Centre) of the Royal National Throat, Nose and Ear Hospital. When she died in 1965 she was busy on a book, also with Professor Fry, directed to the intelligent layman and designed to make available the fundamental facts about hearing and the way it develops both in the normal and in the deaf or hard-of-hearing child. It was not designed as a manual for the parents of deaf children but it was hoped that the principles set out in it would help them to understand the nature of the handicap and their vital part in overcoming it.

As her husband I had found Edith's work with deaf children fascinating to an extent far beyond the natural interest that anyone would take in his wife's profession. I was very keen that her death should not prevent the publication of the projected book and almost immediately started discussions about its completion. In the end I agreed to undertake this myself. Although not professionally involved I had read everything that Edith had written on the subject and had heard her speak about it, both in private and on public platforms.

In *The Deaf Child* Edith Whetnall and Dennis Fry did not indicate which chapters had been contributed by each, although it must be pretty clear to anyone who knows the particular angles from which they approached their common objective. The same anonymity has been followed in this book. Dennis Fry's chapters represent the up-to-date views of an expert in his own field. In the chapters begun by Edith Whetnall and completed by me, I have retained her actual words wherever possible. Where it has been necessary to fill in gaps and provide continuity I have endeavoured to write what I think she would have written herself. The result represents, as nearly as I can make it, the views she held in 1965 after some twenty years of professional, and more than thirty years of personal, experience of deafness in children. No one knows better than I that the chapters are not what she would have written in 1969. Her mind was never static and her opinions and her mode of presenting them were constantly reviewed in the light of further experience.

There is one exception to the anonymity of the chapters. Chapter I is based on Edith's writings and sayings, but it is my own personal account of her work and ideas as I saw them develop.

Dennis Fry has kindly read the chapters that I have completed to eliminate any obvious nonsense that I had introduced. I am however entirely responsible for these chapters and crave the reader's indulgence for the degree to which the text falls short of what Edith Whetnall would have produced if she had lived to complete it.

We do not apologise for any overlap and repetitions. The theme of the book is a simple one—the necessity for both the normal and the deaf child to learn to use his hearing—to 'learn to hear'. This central theme is looked at from a number of angles and some repetition is inevitable if each chapter is to make sense without too much cross-reference to other chapters.

Our gratitude to the authors and publishers who have permitted reproduction of illustrations is acknowledged under the figures. The audiograms were all recorded by staff of the Nuffield Centre or the Audiology Unit. As in *The Deaf Child* all the photographs were taken by Mr. D. Connolly of the Department of Clinical Photography, Institute of Laryngology and Otology and we are grateful for his patience and skill. Figures IX, 3 (*b*), (*c*) and (*d*) were specially taken for *Learning to Hear* and we are grateful to parents and children and also to Miss Pamela Colyer, Administrative Assistant, Nuffield Hearing and Speech Centre, who made all the arrangements for these photographs.

It is a pleasure to acknowledge the helpfulness of the publishers and particularly of Dr. Raymond Greene, who encouraged me to undertake a task which I have found enthralling, as well as difficult. I could not have completed it without the active help and encouragement of my present wife, Anne, who knows how grateful I am to her.

ROBERT NIVEN

CHAPTER I

HOW IT BEGAN

The Editor

Janette was a normal looking baby. She appeared to develop normally. She sat up at the usual age, crawled at the usual age, started to walk at the usual age. But she did not talk. At first no one worried. After all, one of her brothers had talked late but there was nothing wrong with his speech or hearing now.

As the months lengthened into years the family's attempts to reassure itself became less convincing and a dreadful doubt began to grow. Eventually the doubt became so strong that they felt they must settle it. Janette was about three by this time and her mother and aunt took her out for a picnic tea on a heath near their home. The adults sat on the grass and Janette played about. Gradually she wandered off a little way. Then the test began. Her mother and her aunt called out to her, louder and louder, but she took no notice. The only way to attract her attention was to go right up to her. The suspicions had become near certainty and she was taken off to the woman doctor who looked after the family's health. Nothing was said about the suspicion in the minds of the family. The doctor took a long time examining her and then she looked up and asked, "Has it ever occurred to you that Janette might be deaf?"

The word had been spoken. The diagnosis had been made and now began the agonising search for treatment. This all happened about 40 years ago when the orthodox method of training the deaf-born was by lip-reading. It was thought that many deaf-born children were totally deaf, 'stone-deaf', with no hearing at all. It was realised that some had a little hearing but if a child did not have enough hearing to learn speech 'spontaneously' it was assumed that the little bit of hearing present was of no use. As a result, any hearing the child had (*residual hearing*) was ignored in his training. There was a controversy between the advocates of sign language and finger-spelling (the *manual* method) and the advocates of lip-reading (the *oral* method). Lip-reading was the orthodox method in this country although signs were also used to a varying extent, sometimes officially and deliberately, sometimes unofficially. Any use of residual hearing was discouraged as likely to distract from the all-important gazing at the lips. Training was almost entirely in the hands of teachers of the deaf. Doctors did little more than make the diagnosis, after which they passed the children on to the teachers.

1

Lip-reading is a laborious method of communication. The child is taught to watch the face of the person talking and to associate the shape of the lips with the meaning of the words. At the same time, he is taught to put his own lips into the right shape to express sounds and words—and not only his lips, the whole complicated apparatus of speech employing tongue, teeth, palate, vocal cords and muscles of respiration. Progress is slow and the final result is often an adult who can communicate only with other deaf people and with a limited number of hearing people. Janette's mother became adept at communicating with her and conversation in the home circle would be interrupted while Mother mouthed messages so that Janette should not feel left out.

Janette's first teacher was a retired, but very active, headmistress of a school for the deaf, Miss Blanche Neville. Then she went to various schools for the deaf. Her progress was disappointing and after some years Miss Neville took over again. After this progress was more satisfactory but when I first met her at the age of eleven or twelve, I found it impossible to communicate with her. She could not understand me and I could not understand her.

All this time Janette's aunt had been watching from the sidelines, interested in her niece's progress, doing what she could to help from time to time. She was just between schoolgirl and student at the time when Janette's deafness was diagnosed. Soon afterwards, she entered medical school where very early she showed a preference for surgery. Even before she qualified she had decided that she wanted to be an Ear, Nose and Throat surgeon. Undoubtedly, her niece's deafness had something to do with this decision. She had met Janette's teacher, the retired headmistress, who had spoken of the need for more medical interest in the deaf child.

First, she must complete her surgical apprenticeship. There was no special examination for Ear, Nose and Throat surgeons in those days. She did a job as House Surgeon to a general surgical firm in the hospital where she had trained and took the Fellowship of the Royal College of Surgeons by an examination in General Surgery. Then she began to specialise in Ear, Nose and Throat surgery, first as Registrar and finally as a Consultant Surgeon.

By this time, the war had come and passed and Edith herself had been involved in a bad car accident, for Janette's aunt was the late Edith Whetnall, the originator of this book which is being completed by me, her husband, and by Dennis Fry, collaborator in her pioneer work for deaf children. Had Edith lived to complete the book this chapter could not have been written—medical etiquette and Edith's own reticence would have forbidden it.

While she was convalescing from the accident Edith was not idle. I was with her one day when the late Sir Terence Cawthorne came to visit her in her hospital ward. She was still a Registrar and Cawthorne was one of her chiefs. He was also Consultant Aural Surgeon to the London County Council and its School Medical Service. Edith asked if she might attend his clinics for deaf children at County Hall and this was the first work she did when she became well enough.

Children suspected of deafness were referred to these clinics for 'ascertainment', that is, to establish whether or not they were deaf. When deafness was diagnosed a recommendation about education was made. Except for the few families who could afford a private tutor there was in those days only one possible recommendation—education at a deaf school. Changes, however, had begun and when Edith first began attending Terence Cawthorne's clinics he was busy on the creation of Partially Deaf Units. These were small groups of deaf children under a trained teacher of the deaf but in a school for normally hearing children. The deaf children mixed with the normally hearing children for activities like games and physical education. The aim of the Units was to integrate the deaf children as far as possible with the normally hearing children. Whenever possible the deaf children passed on from the Partially Deaf Units to full membership of the ordinary classes for normally hearing children. As in so may other fields of human endeavour, the results depended largely on the calibre of the staff involved—especially on the teacher of the deaf in the Unit and the head teacher of the hearing school.

The end of the war saw many new developments in all sorts of fields. There had been advances in electronics during the war and better hearing aids were being developed. The Royal National Throat, Nose and Ear Hospital decided to start a clinic specially devoted to deaf patients. It was perhaps typical of the mental attitude of those days that it was called the 'Deafness Aid Clinic'. Edith had become an Assistant Surgeon to the Hospital in 1946, and in 1947 she was appointed first Director of the Deafness Aid Clinic. The clinic began in a basement room in the Golden Square branch of the Hospital not far from Regent Street and the underground line between Oxford Circus and Piccadilly. Edith Whetnall did a few sessions a week along with her surgical work and there was one full-time technician. At times the basement flooded and they had to retreat until the floods subsided.

A major part of the work of the Deafness Aid Clinic was the fitting of hearing aids to deaf adults and teaching them how to get the most benefit from their aids—'auditory training' or 'auditory rehabilitation'. From the start, however, Edith Whetnall was determined to do something for the deaf person with the most grievous handicap—the deaf-born child. She had now succeeded

Terence Cawthorne at County Hall as Consultant Aural Surgeon to the School Medical Service. There she had met John Blount, Headmaster of Rayners School for children who had some other handicap as well as deafness. He was also Inspector of Schools for the Deaf for the L.C.C. and Edith Whetnall had been impressed by the advantages of having his educational point of view on the problems that came up in the ascertainment clinic. She therefore pressed for the appointment of a teacher of the deaf to the Deafness Aid Clinic. She was a persuasive advocate and she had two allies in John Young, House Governor of the Hospital, and Frank Ormerod, Chairman of the Medical Committee and later Professor in the newly formed Institute of Laryngology and Otology. Together they laid the foundations of what was eventually to become the Nuffield Hearing and Speech Centre.

All the hearing aids issued in those days were commercial aids. A year after the start of the Deafness Aid Clinic came the National Health Service and the Government 'Medresco' aid. The clinic was swamped with a rush of applicants for the new 'free' aids and Edith used to look back with thankfulness to the first year of comparative peace when she had a chance to learn from the children she saw. There were fifty-seven the first year. The approach at first was based on the usual assumptions of the time—the severely deaf child could not learn to talk through hearing and any child who had not learnt to talk by the age of two or three would never learn to talk through his hearing. He must be taught through lip-reading. This meant that the diagnosis of deafness was automatically followed by a recommendation for admission to a school for the deaf as soon as the child reached the appropriate age.

It all seemed simple and straightforward. The process of education would be lengthy and complicated and would demand all the dedication and skill possessed by the teachers of the deaf but the decision the otologist had to make about the child's education appeared simple. Then along came some children whose condition challenged the assumptions underlying the decisions.

These children had severe hearing losses. Measurements of hearing with an audiometer showed losses as great as those of children in schools for the deaf. The surprising thing was that these children could talk and could understand the speech of others. They were attending schools for normally hearing children and managing to hold their own. It all seemed wrong and the natural response was to think that it could not last. The education of the children might suffer if they stayed on in hearing schools. Was it not the otologist's duty to advise transfer to a school for the deaf?

Well, before doing this, one had better make sure how the children were doing in their present hearing environment. The parents might be

biased. What did the teachers think? Reports on educational progress
were requested from the schools and were found to be satisfactory.
These children—or their parents—had done something that the
experts thought was impossible.

I have a vivid recollection of Edith coming home with stories of
these children and of how interested and excited she was. By this
time she had secured the collaboration of Dennis Fry, then Reader,
and now Professor of Experimental Phonetics in the University of
London. They puzzled over these children together. "Well anyhow,"
he said, "whether we can explain it or not, we have to accept the
fact that it has happened."

Sir Geoffrey Jefferson, the brain surgeon, once gave the inaugural
address at the beginning of the academic year at the Institute of
Laryngology and Otology. He said that people could be divided into
two groups by their reaction to a new fact which appeared to
contradict all their accepted ideas. The reaction could be "Hell!" or
"Well?". The first group were angry at the challenge to their comfortably held ideas. They were no use as research workers; they would
indeed obstruct the research of others. The second group immediately
began to think about the meaning of the new fact, how to test if it
really was a fact, how to revise the established ideas to fit in with the
new fact.

Fortunately for the deaf child, Edith Whetnall belonged to the
second group and so did Dennis Fry. What could be the explanation
of these children who had succeeded without professional help where
other children had failed in spite of professional help?

One of the first of these children was G.M. He was five years old
when he attended the clinic. He had meningitis when he was twelve
months old. One of the complications of meningitis is deafness and
G.M. became deaf. At the age of two years he had been given a
hearing aid. His audiogram is shown in Figure I.1. Audiograms will
be discussed in more detail in a later chapter but it does not require
specialised knowledge to see that G.M.'s audiogram shows a
considerable degree of deafness. In spite of this he had good speech
and good comprehension of speech. He was at an ordinary school.
So ingrained was the idea that deaf children should be in deaf
schools that he had been referred to the clinic for advice about
continuing in an ordinary school. There was no hesitation in
recommending that he should do so but perhaps he was an isolated
case; perhaps the reason why he had done so well was that he had
had normal hearing for the first year of life and that his first year's
listening to speech had been the basis of his surprising success.

Further experience showed that he was not an isolated case.
Along came other children with similar stories. Some of these had
undoubtedly been born deaf and had not had G.M.'s advantage of a

whole year's listening practice before becoming deaf. So that was not the explanation. The type of hearing loss varied from child to child. E.P., for example (see Figure I.2), had a complete loss of hearing for high frequencies, that is for high pitched sounds. It will

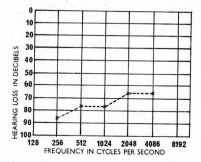

Figure I.1. Audiogram of G.M. (see page 5)
(*Reproduced from 'The Deaf Child', Edith Whetnall and D. B. Fry,*
William Heinemann Medical Books, London.)

be seen later that these high frequencies are particularly important for the recognition of consonants. Nevertheless, she had 'spontaneous' speech, although with a slight speech defect. She was at an ordinary school and doing well. She had been referred to the clinic

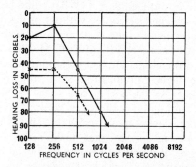

Figure I.2. Audiogram of E.P.
(*Reproduced from 'The Deaf Child', Edith Whetnall and D. B. Fry,*
William Heinemann Medical Books, London.)

so that she might have a hearing aid, do even better and make sure of keeping her place in the ordinary school.

What could be the explanation of the success that had been obtained with these children without any specialised training? The answer was always the same. They had not had any specialised or professional training but it was far from true that they had not had any training at all. Their mothers had realised at an early age, usually in the first or second year, that their children were deaf. They had then done what appeared to them to be the natural thing. They had each drawn her child close to her and spoken into the ear. As a result all the children developed speech 'spontaneously' and understood speech. They had indeed had training, 'auditory training', but it had been done, not by a teacher, not by a doctor, not by a hearing therapist, but by 'Mum'.

The reports from the ordinary schools they were attending were always good and it was of course advised that they should continue at their ordinary school. I write 'of course' but there was no 'of course' about it in those days. The following example illustrates the attitude towards deafness about that time. A girl was referred to the ascertainment clinic at County Hall. She had won a scholarship to the University from the ordinary school in which she had been educated. The regulations required her to be medically examined and it was discovered—for the first time—that she was deaf. Her audiogram is shown in Figure I.3. The immediate official reaction was that she was not fit to take up her scholarship. Edith Whetnall had no doubts. If the girl could overcome her disability to such an

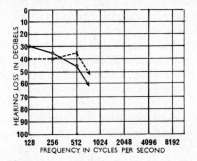

Figure I.3.
(*Reproduced from 'The Deaf Child', Edith Whetnall and D. B. Fry,*
William Heinemann Medical Books, London.)

extent that the disability was not recognised at her school and she had won a scholarship, then she was certainly fit to enjoy the fruits of her efforts and take up her scholarship.

The news got about among parents that you could take your deaf child to the Deafness Aid Clinic without having him automatically whisked away to a deaf school. More parents therefore dared to bring along their deaf children whom they had trained to hear and to speak. The pattern in each case was the same and each case was further evidence for the new attitude and the new approach to the problems of congenital deafness that was being developed at the Deafness Aid Clinic.

Work continued along two lines. The literature was searched for any accounts of similar happenings in the past and attempts were made to reproduce in other children the successes brought off by the unaided action of the mothers of these phenomenal children.

One previous report in the literature was close at hand, in Cyril Burt's great study of children in L.C.C. schools. In *The Backward Child*, published in 1937, he commented on the fact that 'here and there, it may often be observed that a child who is severely deaf is able to make good progress in the ordinary school'.

Further study showed that as long ago as 1761 there had been a demonstration of the fact that auditory perception increased in deaf children when they were given constant practice in listening. Away back in pre-Revolution Paris, the Paris of Louis XV and Madame de Pompadour, the Paris of the *Salons* and the Encyclopaedists, Ernaud had made the demonstration before the Academy of Sciences. The demonstration had been repeated, again and again, by otologists in various countries but their results had been largely ignored or disbelieved by other doctors and by the schools for the deaf. It is not an uncommon fate for new ideas. Semmelweiss, who introduced the antiseptic technique to combat puerperal fever, was driven from his post in Vienna. Mendel's work on genetics was ignored in his lifetime and revived only long after his death.

Side by side with this research into the writings of the past went the repeated demonstration that quite small amounts of residual hearing could be useful if the child was trained to use it instead of being trained to ignore it and to concentrate on the purely visual approach of lip-reading.

Children were picked out who had hearing losses of about the same degree as the deaf children with 'spontaneous' speech. It was beginning to be realised that young children have a greater facility for learning speech than older children. Attempts were therefore made to detect deafness early and auditory training was started with younger and younger children. It was not possible to carry out audiograms on these very young children, so tests were made with the voice and with other sounds. The children selected at first were those who at their first test of hearing showed a response to sounds at a distance of about 8 to 10 feet and to the voice 'at the meatus', i.e., close-up to the ear.

These children were supplied with hearing aids. The younger they were, the more readily they took to them. The parents were encouraged to talk to them. They attended the Clinic for advice and help from the otologist and the teacher of the deaf. The aid of teachers in hearing schools was enlisted. As a result of all these measures many of the children learnt speech in a manner which surprised Edith Whetnall herself. The experiment had worked and the Clinic had reproduced the successes of the mothers of the children with 'spontaneous' speech, the success of the children whom Burt had observed here and there in the L.C.C. schools and the successes of forgotten pioneers from Ernaud onwards.

New advances and discoveries seldom take place in complete isolation and Edith Whetnall was soon delighted to find accounts of similar work in contemporary medical literature as well as in the writings of the past. In Holland, Sweden, America, reports appeared of successes in training the remaining fragments or islands of hearing in deaf-born children. When one of these foreigners visited London Edith was amused to hear a colleague's comment, "Why, he is saying all the the things that Edith Whetnall says." "A prophet is not without honour save in his own country" and it was a great asset to all these workers that their successes were not isolated but were reproduced in other countries.

The successes had come from the ability to observe the reactions of deaf children and the willingness and courage to try a new approach. This new approach was based on the way in which normal individuals learn to understand and produce speech. The next few chapters attempt to give a brief account of the anatomy, physiology and psychology of hearing and speech.

CHAPTER II

THE EAR AND HOW IT WORKS

We all know that our ears *receive* sounds which come towards us from the outside world. They do more than this. They also *transform* the sounds, which arrive as pressure waves in the air and are changed in the ear into electrical waves travelling along the acoustic or auditory nerves to the brain.

Like so many other important parts of the body, the ears are paired organs. They are situated symmetrically on either side of the head. Each ear (Figure II.1) consists of three parts—outer, middle

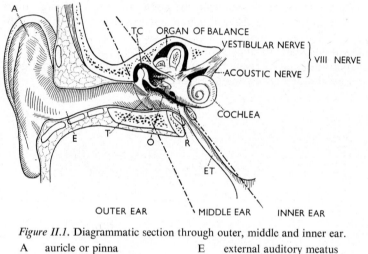

Figure II.1. Diagrammatic section through outer, middle and inner ear.

A	auricle or pinna	E	external auditory meatus
T	tympanic membrane or eardrum	T.C.	tympanic cavity or middle ear
E.T.	Eustachian tube		
O	fenestra ovalis or oval window	R	fenestra rotunda or round window

After 'Speech and Hearing', Harvey Fletcher, Macmillan, London.

and inner. The *outer ear* is divided into two parts, the auricle or pinna and the external auditory meatus. The *auricle* or *pinna* is the only part which is completely external to the skull. In man it has dwindled to a small vestige compared with the much larger auricles of the lower animals. It is vestigial not only in size but in structure. The auricle of lower animals is provided with muscles which move it into the best position for detecting and localising sounds. The human auricle does possess some muscles but they are only puny reminders of the muscles of other animals. A few people can twitch their ears enough to make it an interesting party trick but for all practical purposes the human auricle is a small, motionless funnel.

These differences in structure reflect a great difference in the function of hearing in man and other animals. In other animals the main function of hearing is protective. The animal needs to be able to hear the faintest sound which may mean danger. It needs, too, to be able to tell the direction from which the sound is coming, and so to know in what direction the possibly dangerous cause of the sound is to be found. The huge mobile funnel-shaped auricle is of obvious assistance in these processes of detection and localisation. It is rather like an early form of the rotating saucers on radar systems which also give early warning of the approach of danger.

The vestigial funnel of the human auricle does perform a slight function of collecting sound and directing it onwards to the middle and inner ear, but this is relatively unimportant in human hearing. In man the most important part of hearing is the fine discrimination and association which goes on in the brain and enables us to communicate by speech. Communication is overwhelmingly the most important function of human hearing.

From the depths of the auricle, whether large and mobile, or small and inert, a tube passes inwards to the middle ear. This tube is the ear hole or *external auditory meatus* (Latin—*meatus* = passage). It is about one inch long. The outer third is made of cartilage (gristle) continuous with the cartilaginous core of the auricle. The inner two thirds is a bony tube. The whole of the external auditory meatus is lined with skin. The skin in the cartilaginous part contains hairs and also ceruminous glands which secrete the 'cerumen' or wax, which in excess can block the meatus and cause a considerable amount of deafness.

At the inner end of the tubular external auditory meatus is the tympanic membrane or drumhead which separates the outer ear from the *middle ear* or *tympanic cavity*. This is a slit just over half an inch from front to back and from top to bottom. The narrowest part of the slit is opposite the centre of the tympanic membrane where it is about one tenth of an inch wide (about the thickness of a florin). The middle ear is lined with mucous membrane like the inside of the mouth and is filled with air which reaches it through the narrow Eustachian tube from the back of the pharynx behind the nose. It is because of this communicating tube that we feel our eardrums 'pop' when we close our mouths, pinch our nostrils and attempt to breathe out. The existence of this tube is also the reason why air hostesses bring round trays of sweets and chewing-gum at take-off and landing. As we go rapidly up or down the atmospheric pressure alters while the pressure of the air in the middle ear remains much the same. This difference in pressure between the middle ear and the outside atmosphere causes the well-known feeling of discomfort in the ears during ascent and descent. Swallowing causes a reflex opening of the Eustachian tube and allows the pressure in the middle ear to become the same as that in the outside atmosphere; as we swallow we feel the discomfort disappear only to reappear as the altitude changes until we swallow again.

A similar but lesser discomfort is experienced even with the much smaller changes in altitude and pressure involved in travelling in the lift to and from a deep underground railway, as at Hampstead station. At the other extreme, rapid descents in aircraft or by deep sea divers may lead to haemorrhage into the middle ear or rupture of the eardrum.

The tympanic cavity or middle ear contains a chain of tiny bones or *ossicles* which transmit the vibrations of the tympanic membrane or ear drum across the middle ear to the inner ear (Figure II.2).

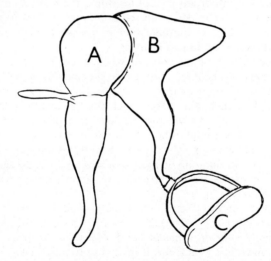

Figure II.2. The ossicles of the middle ear.
A, malleus or hammer; B, incus or anvil; C, stapes or stirrup.
(*Reproduced with permission from 'Hearing in Man and Animals',*
R. T. Beatty, Bell, London.)

These ossicles have Latin names which describe their shape or function. The *malleus* (hammer) is shaped somewhat like a small hammer with its handle attached to the tympanic membrane and its head forming a joint with the *incus* or anvil. The incus is not really shaped very like an anvil but the hammer may be thought of as beating on it. In fact the malleus and incus are joined together so the hammer does not really beat on the anvil. Nevertheless the name is perhaps not too far fetched. A projection of the incus forms a joint with the *stapes* (stirrup) which really does look like a stirrup. The two curved arms of the stapes are joined by a footplate of bone which fits into an opening in the wall of the inner ear. This opening is called the *fenestra ovalis* or 'oval window'.

The *inner ear* is the most complicated part of the ear. It lies in very dense bone which forms part of the temporal bone of the skull. Because of its density this bone is known as the *petrous* (or 'stony') portion of the temporal bone. The inner ear consists of a series of intercommunicating sacs and canals (the *membranous labyrinth*) lying in a series of spaces in the petrous bone (the *bony labyrinth*). The name labyrinth is applied to these structures because of their complicated, almost mazelike, shape. The bony labyrinth is filled with a fluid called perilymph. The membranous labyrinth lies suspended in the perilymph. Its walls consist of membranes and it is filled with a fluid called endolymph.

Not all the structures in the labyrinth are concerned with hearing. Some have to do with balance so that it is not surprising that hearing and balance are sometimes upset in the same disease, for example, Ménière's Disease. The hearing apparatus has evolved from an organ that is concerned almost entirely with balance in the fish.

The part of the labyrinth concerned with hearing is the *cochlea*. This is the Latin for 'snail' and the cochlea is a spiral tube rather like a snail's shell (Figure II.3). Inside the bony cochlea is the membranous cochlea or cochlear duct. Like the rest of the membranous labyrinth it is filled with endolymph and surrounded by perilymph. The floor of the cochlear duct is called the basilar membrane and on it lies the *organ of Corti*. This organ of Corti contains a number of *hair-cells*, so-called because each of them ends in about twenty hair-like processes lying in the interior of the cochlear duct. At the other end each hair cell forms connections with a multitude of nerve fibres which pass inwards towards the acoustic or cochlear nerve which runs in the bony core of the cochlea. It is certain that it is in the hair cells that the final transformation takes place by which the air pressure changes of the sound waves are converted into the electrical nerve impulses which pass from the cochlea along the acoustic nerve to the brain.

There has already been an intermediate transformation of the sound waves which reached the outer ear in the form of changes in air pressure. These air pressure changes have been converted into

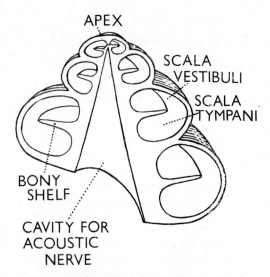

Figure II.3. Section through the bony cochlea.
(*Reproduced with permission from 'Hearing in Man and Animals',*
R. T. Beatty, Bell, London.')

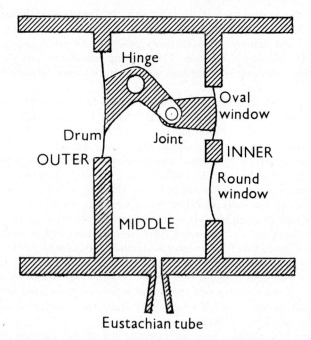

Figure II.4. Diagram to show the relations of the three divisions of the
ear. The outer and middle ears contain air, while the inner ear is filled
with liquid.
(*Reproduced with permission from 'Hearing in Man and Animals',*
R. T. Beatty, Bell, London.)

changes in fluid pressure in the perilymph and endolymph (Figure II.4). As the cochlear duct coils round the central bony core of the snail-like cochlea it has above and below it spaces called the *scala vestibuli* and the *scala tympani* (Figure II.5). The whole is enclosed by the dense bony labyrinth except at two points where there are

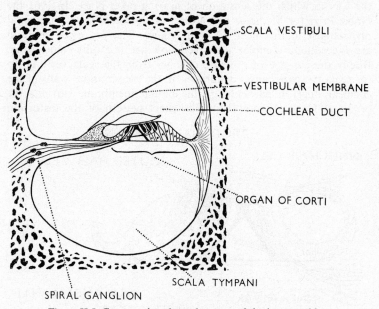

Figure II.5. Cross-section through a turn of the bony cochlea.
*After 'The Ciba Collection of Medical Illustrations', Volume I,
F. Netter, Ciba, New Jersey.*

openings between the bony labyrinth and the middle ear. Only at these openings or 'windows' is any movement possible in the membranous walls of the labyrinth, in the scala vestibuli at the oval window and in the scala tympani at the round window. You will remember how the footplate of the stapes fits into the oval window. Sound waves impinge on the eardrum and cause it to vibrate. This movement is transmitted through the chain of ossicles to the footplate of the stapes and as the footplate moves in and out it carries with it the wall of the scala vestibuli and causes changes in pressure in the fluid inside it. These changes are transmitted across the cochlear duct to the scala tympani and the membranous wall at the round window moves in and out in the opposite direction to the movements at the oval window. In the form of deafness known as *otosclerosis* the footplate of the stapes becomes fixed, so that the process just described can not take place. Various operations are done for the relief of otosclerosis, such as fenestration (the formation of a new window or 'fenestra') and stapedectomy; all depend on overcoming in one way or another the mechanical impediment to the transmission of sound pressure changes in the air to the fluids in the inner ear.

Many conflicting theories have been put forward to account for the way in which the sensation of hearing takes place. In 1961 the Nobel Prize for Medicine was given to an outstanding experimental physiologist in this field, G. von Békésy. The processes involved are exceedingly complex and even now are not fully understood. Briefly the passage of pressure changes from the scala vestibuli to the scala tympani causes distortions in the membranous walls of the cochlear duct, in particular in the basilar membrane carrying the organ of Corti (Figure II.6). The exact pattern of the distortion

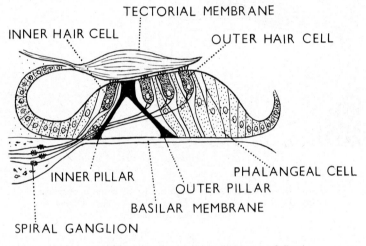

Figure II.6. Cross-section through the organ of Corti.
After 'The Ciba Collection of Medical Illustrations', Volume I,
F. Netter, Ciba, New Jersey.

depends on the frequency and intensity of the sound impinging on the ear. The distortion is appreciated by the hair cells, probably in a manner similar to the perception of light touch through the hairs of the skin. The innervation of the hair cells is complex. Each of the inner row of hair cells is connected to one or two fibres of the acoustic nerve and each nerve fibre is connected to one or two inner hair cells. In the outer rows of hair cells more hair cells are connected to each nerve fibre and more fibres to each hair cell. There are over 15,000 hair cells and about 27,000 nerve fibres. If we consider the apparently inexhaustible permutations and combinations of 50 to 60 pairs of teams in a football pool, it is not difficult to conceive that the organ of Corti and the acoustic nerve have the capacity for a very detailed analysis of the sounds which reach them. This is not the same as saying that it is easy to understand the mechanism by which this analysis takes place, and there is still much scope for extension of knowledge about this.

The acoustic nerve joins the vestibular nerve which is concerned with balance and both run together as the VIIIth cranial nerve to the stalk of nervous tissue which passes upwards from the spinal cord to the brain. The nerve fibres starting from the hair cells in the organ of Corti do not pass without interruption to their final destination in the cortex or outer layer of the brain. At various places on the way are relay stations where the fibres end, making connections with other nerve cells from which fibres run on to the next relay station. It has been shown that there is a progressive increase in the number of nerve fibres at each relay station which provides still more possibilities for permutations and combinations. About half of the fibres cross over from one side to the other in the stalk of the brain, so that each cochlea is represented equally in the cortex or outer layer of both sides of the brain. This means that deafness is rarely caused by disease or damage in the cerebral cortex. In a very extensive experience of deafness in children EW saw only one such case, a child who had suffered from an injury affecting the auditory centres in the cortex on both sides.

Although auditory sensation in the cerebral cortex is two-sided, this is not true of the centre controlling speech which is called *Broca's area*, after the French surgeon who first described it. This area is situated close to the auditory cortex and to the part of the motor cortex controlling the muscles of the face, tongue and larynx.

CHAPTER III

WE HEAR WITH OUR BRAINS

Chapter II ended with the arrival at the cerebral cortex of nerve fibres from the ear. But just what is the *cerebral cortex*? The brain consists of two great masses of nervous tissue, rather like a roughly shaped ball split down the middle. These two masses are the cerebral hemispheres. They are connected with the spinal cord and with the sensory and motor nerves throughout the body by the brain stalk which divides into two cerebral peduncles, one to each hemisphere. Each hemisphere is also connected to the other by nerve fibres passing in a bridge of tissue at the bottom of the cleft or fissure which separates them.

Examination of a cross-section of a cerebral hemisphere shows that it is divided into a central core of white matter and an outer layer or *cortex* (Latin = 'bark') of grey matter. The white matter is made up of nerve fibres passing from sensory nerve endings to the cortex or from the cortex to the motor endings in muscles or from one part of the cortex to another. The cortex consists of highly specialised nerve cells ('the little grey cells' so proudly mentioned by Agatha Christie's famous detective, Hercule Poirot).

In birds and reptiles which are low in the evolutionary scale the cortex presents a smooth unbroken surface covering the cerebral hemispheres. In the human foetus we find the same smooth cortex up to the end of the fourth month of intra-uterine development. After this time localised depressions appear which deepen to form grooves known as *sulci* or furrows. In between the furrows are the *gyri* or convolutions. Some of the sulci are so deep that their existence has been used to divide each cerebral hemisphere into a number of lobes, for ease of description. These are the frontal, temporal, parietal and occipital lobes (Figure III.1.a). The indented shape of the cortex obviously means that the total extent of the cortical layer in the human brain is relatively much greater than its extent in animals with a smooth or less convoluted cortex. As 'Alpha of the Plough' imote, it is not the size of the brain but its convolutions that are wrportant, and in general there is a relationship between the intelligence of a species of animal and the degree of convolution of its cerebral cortex.

Partly as the result of experiment and partly by observation of the effects of disease in different parts of the cortex it has been possible to map out clearly the function of some parts of the cortex, although the areas for which we have really precise knowledge are limited in

18

extent. The visual cortex is in the occipital lobe, right at the back of it. The motor cortex and the cortex connected with general sensation lie close to the *central sulcus* which separates the frontal and parietal lobes. In front of the central sulcus, in the *precentral gyrus*, is the *motor cortex*. Behind it, in the *post-central gyrus*, is the *sensory cortex*. More or less at right angles to the central sulcus is the

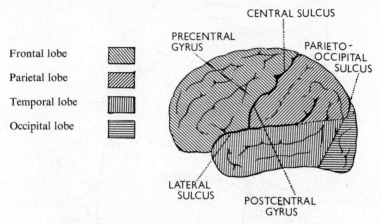

Frontal lobe

Parietal lobe

Temporal lobe

Occipital lobe

Figure III.1. (a) and (b). Diagrammatic side-views of left cerebral hemisphere.
Modified from 'Cunningham's Manual of Practical Anatomy'
(ed. G. J. Romanes), 13th Edition, O.U.P., London.

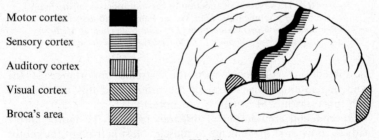

Motor cortex

Sensory cortex

Auditory cortex

Visual cortex

Broca's area

Figure III 1 (b)

lateral fissure below which lies the temporal lobe. Immediately below the central fissure is the *auditory cortex*, situated in the superior temporal gyrus (Figure III.1.b).

Not only has it been possible to pick out which part of the cortex controls motor activity, i.e. which is the motor cortex, but it is also possible to tell which parts of the body are controlled from different parts of the motor cortex. The parts of the body are represented upside down, with the feet at the upper part of the precentral gyrus and the head at the lower end, near to the lateral fissure and the auditory cortex (Figure III.2). A highly significant fact is that the hand and the head, especially the face and lips, have far more than a fair share of the motor cortex. Indeed, together, they take up about as much space as the whole of the rest of the body. This

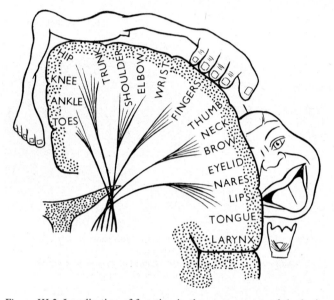

Figure III.2. Localisation of function in the motor cortex of the brain: the motor homunculus—after Wilder Penfield and associates. (*Reproduced with permission from 'The Ciba Collection of Medical Illustrations', Volume I, F. Netter, Ciba, New Jersey.*)

undoubtedly is connected with the extreme importance of the hand in handling objects and of the mouth and lips in speech—both functions in which man is pre-eminent.

Experimental stimulation of different parts of the motor cortex leads to individual movements of muscles. Just in front of the motor cortex is another area which appears to be associated with the control of more complicated series of movements—for example, putting on and buttoning up a coat—done without thought by the adult but laboriously learnt by the child. The same applies to the control of the complicated mechanism of speech. This is carried out in Broca's area which is situated in the frontal lobe just in front of the part of the motor cortex dealing with the muscles involved in speech and not far from the auditory cortex. As was stated above, this area is not present on both sides of the brain. The side on which it is situated depends on whether the individual is right- or left-handed. The motor fibres largely cross over on their passage from the brain to the motor cells in the spinal cord so that the motor cortex in the left cerebral hemisphere controls the right side of the body and vice versa. In the right-handed person Broca's area is in the left hemisphere; in the left-handed in the right hemisphere. This shows itself very clearly in patients who have had a stroke, a partial paralysis due to haemorrhage into the brain. Sometimes the patient is not only unable to move his limbs on the affected side but is also unable to express himself by speech—a condition known as *motor aphasia*. He may understand perfectly what is said to him and may be able to move the muscles of speech but he cannot express himself. This happens when the haemorrhage involves Broca's area or the fibres leading from it. The right-handed man may develop aphasia if he has a stroke involving the left cerebral hemisphere—the left-handed will have aphasia only if he has the haemorrhage in the right cerebral hemisphere. If Broca's area is damaged in a child before speech is established, the corresponding area in the other hemisphere will take over the functions of speech control.

The function of the other areas of the cerebral cortex is not nearly so precisely known. They are often referred to as the *association areas* and it is thought that they may be the seats of the various psychological processes that we describe as learning, remembering, deciding, and so on. The mechanism of these processes is still obscure but the numerous inter-connections between various nerve cells and fibres must play an important part in all mental activity including the understanding of speech. It is for this reason that so much space has been devoted to a description of the brain. The most perfect ear is useless as an organ of hearing without the activity of the brain to recognise and interpret the impulses conveyed to it along the auditory nerve. "No! She's not deaf," said an otologist of our acquaintance about a patient who had been referred to him. "She's just got nothing to register with." On the other hand the brain can make use of imperfect clues fed into it from a defective ear. The activity of the brain is the most important factor in the long process by which the infant and the young child learns to walk, to dress and feed himself, and to understand and produce speech. This is the basis of the training of the child with defective hearing whose brain can enable him to overcome his handicap if he is given the right help at the right time by the adults around him.

EVOLUTION OF HEARING

Many animals use sound for purposes of communication. The traveller in the Swiss Alps hears the piercing whistle by which the marmot warns its mates of approaching danger. Birds use sound to call their mates or to warn away intruders. Baby birds call loudly for food. Different sounds are used to convey a variety of meanings. The sounds made by a hen, for example, enable us to tell very easily whether she is brooding, leading a group of feeding chickens or making the triumphant announcement that she has just laid an egg.

The most complicated animal communication, however, is almost infinitely simpler than the complexity and flexibility of human speech. The emergence of speech so late in the evolutionary chain is probably the main feature which separates man from the lower animals. It is dependent almost entirely on the complexity of the human cortex described above, but there has also been an evolution in the peripheral organ of hearing—the ear.

Speech makes use of parts of the body which were primarily devoted to other functions: breathing, chewing, swallowing. The *organ of hearing* serves no other purpose but as we have seen it is closely connected with the organ of balance. The ear of vertebrate animals, including man, can be traced back to an organ in fishes which really has more to do with balance than with hearing. It is however capable of detecting sound waves carried in the water.

Great changes were necessary when land animals evolved from the fishes, because the acoustic properties of air and fluid are very different. Sounds do not pass readily from the one medium to the other. In addition air-borne sound waves are reflected from a rigid surface such as the bone or cartilage which encloses the rudimentary inner ear of the fish. One of the first evolutionary changes was the thinning down of an area of this rigid wall and the eventual replacement of the bone or cartilage by a flexible membrane. On the outer side of this membrane developed the middle ear cavity and its enclosed chain of ossicles, which transform the air waves impinging on the ear-drum into fluid waves in the inner ear. At the same time the inner ear developed from a simple cavity into the complicated cochlea—far more complicated than the brief description of it given above and capable of discriminating sounds of different pitch. An odd fact about the cochlea is that the numbers of coils in the spiral differs from species to species without any relationship to the size or intelligence of the animal or its ability to discriminate sounds.

Much experimental work has been done on the hearing of different species of animals. Birds have a great ability to discriminate sounds and reproduce them. This is true not only of the well known 'talking' birds such as the parrot and the mynah. It has also been shown that the robin and many other song birds learn the specific characteristics of their song from the birds that they hear about the time of fledging. Normally these are the parents and there is a sudden increase in the cock robin's song at this time. If, however, the young bird is removed from its parents it will learn the song of the other birds it hears. This was reported by Aristotle. Barrington who corresponded with Gilbert White of Selborne also gave an example: "I educated a young robin under a very fine nightingale; which, however, began already to be out of song and was perfectly mute in less than a fortnight. This robin afterwards sung three parts in four nightingale; and the rest of his song was what the bird-catchers call rubbish, or no particular note whatsoever."* Presumably there is a special facility for learning the songs at this early age comparable to the special facility for learning speech shown by the infant and young child.

Pavlov's discovery of the conditioned reflex is well known. He developed a technique by which he could measure the secretion of gastric juice when a dog was fed. He then associated some other stimulus, such as the ringing of a bell, with the act of feeding. Eventually the dog produced as much gastric juice in response to the false 'conditioned' stimulus as to the actual process of feeding. By varying the stimulus he was able to show the degree of the difference in sound which the dog could discriminate. He found that dogs could distinguish notes only a quarter of a semitone apart. They also could detect differences in loudness and in rhythm of sounds which were beyond the powers of human discrimination.

LEARNING TO HEAR

The development of the cochlea has an interesting parallel in the development of the larynx. A larynx capable of producing speech had evolved long before speech developed and the cochlea of some lower animals is capable of greater sound discrimination than is actually needed for the reception of speech.

The function of hearing in man and other animals is so different that it is unfortunate that we have only the one word 'hearing' to describe both. Although some communication occurs by hearing even in lower animals, the function of hearing is largely protective. Sounds are mainly warnings of impending danger. The faintest sound must be heard, localised and acted upon quickly, without time for thought. Picture a quietly feeding hare. A faint sound reaches it. Immediately the ears prick, the head is raised and the eyes turn towards the source of the sound. Muscles tense and the hare is poised ready for flight if the sound is repeated. All this activity is almost entirely reflex. The nerve centres co-ordinating these actions

* Quoted by David Lack, "The Life of the Robin", (Penguin Books, London, 1953).

are in the brain stem. Very few nerve fibres from the ear pass beyond the brain stem into the cerebral cortex. Indeed hearing and vision are scantily represented in the cortex of the lower mammal; smell is the dominant sense and a large part of the cortex is devoted to it. With the appearance of tree-climbing monkeys and apes hearing and vision become more important, but even with the relatively large acoustic areas in the cortex of apes attempts to teach them speech have largely failed. It was possible to train 'Bonny' the chimpanzee astronaut to carry out various assigned tasks but not possible to explain to her the significance of the space project in which she was participating.

In man there has been an enormous expansion of the cortex of the brain. The exact mechanisms in the brain are still largely obscure in spite of many advances in our understanding. It is however obvious that the vastly enlarged cerebral cortex provides a storehouse of nerve cells in which information can be retained. The numerous interconnections between different parts of the brain enable various items of information to be correlated with other items. Nerve fibres arising from the human ear pass up beyond the centres in the brain stem to end in the greatly enlarged auditory area in the temporal lobe. But it is not just the enlarged temporal cortex which underlies the development of speech. It is also the correlation of auditory information with information provided by the other senses and stored in the cortex. Anyone learning a foreign language knows that understanding of the language comes far sooner than the ability to express one's thoughts in the new language. The child, too, understands before he produces speech. In the same way the evolution of speech must depend on the evolution of hearing. The form of hearing involved in the understanding of speech is so much more complicated than the reflex protective hearing of lower animals that we need a new name for it. One suggestion is 'comprehension' hearing.

It is well known that the stages of evolution are re-enacted in the developing embryo. The heart of the embryo, for example, goes through phases in which it resembles the less complicated heart of the frog and other lower animals. Congenital heart disease occurs when development becomes arrested or distorted. One can see a similar physiological re-enactment of evolution in the development of hearing in the infant after birth. At birth the only hearing present in the human is of a reflex type analogous to the protective hearing of the lower animals. It is central to the whole concept of auditory training to realise that no infant is born with the comprehension hearing which is essential for the understanding and production of speech. This more sophisticated type of hearing is acquired by learning and the child with 'normal hearing' has to learn it just as much as the child who is 'born deaf'. The 'deafness' makes the learning process more difficult and the 'deaf' child needs more conscious help, but the essential process is the same and a child born with 'normal hearing' may fail to develop comprehension hearing, may fail to learn speech, if he is deprived of the conditions which are essential for the learning process to take place.

An understanding of the process of 'learning to hear' is also necessary if tests of hearing in the infant are to be understood and correctly interpreted.

THE INFANT'S RESPONSES TO SOUND

In the new-born infant responses to sounds are entirely reflex—the so-called 'startle responses'. These are elicited only by loud sounds. One response is a twitch or blink of the upper eyelids—the 'cochleo-palpebral reflex', which gets its name from the fact that the stimulus goes via the cochlea and the response is carried out by the muscles of the *palpebra* or eyelids. With a very loud sound there is more than just a blink of the eyelids. There is a general jerking of the body known as the 'general acoustic muscle reflex'.

In the ladder of evolution the cerebral cortex comes to control the response to auditory stimuli (Figure III.3). The reflex centres in the brain stem show a progressive subordination as evolution proceeds from the lower animals towards man. Some of the reflex paths disappear. This is a selective process for some reflexes still perform a useful function. One of the paths that goes is the one leading to the ear muscles from the superior olive (a mass of nerve cells shaped like an olive and situated in the brain stem); at the same time the twitch reflex of the auricle or external ear disappears. The reflex path connecting the eye muscles and the superior olive remains, as co-ordination between the eye and the ear is still necessary. This reflex connection between ear and eye can be seen in the infant. Long before he is able to lift up his head and turn it towards the source of a sound he will turn his eyes in the direction of many sounds.

In lower animals the terminal station for most of the nerve fibres from the ears is the inferior colliculus. In man the bulk of the fibres pass by a different route to the cerebral cortex. The inferior colliculus shrinks in size and receives only a small bundle of nerve fibres possibly subserving only the reflex type of response that makes us leap—we hope to safety—when we suddenly hear a nearby motor-horn.

This evolutionary replacement of reflex, brain-stem activity by the activity of the cerebral cortex finds its counterpart in the gradual subordination of reflex to learnt responses in the growing infant (Figure III.4). From the age of about $2\frac{1}{2}$ months a loud sound

2

produces a less and less brisk blink and general muscle jerk. The general muscle jerk disappears sooner than the blink. If the sound stimulus is presented three times one can see the effects of the process of inhibition which is taking place. The first response is brisk, the second almost as brisk, but the third may be less brisk because of the commencement of inhibition. As the infant grows older the

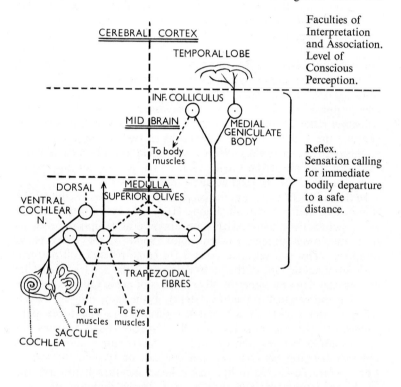

Figure III.3. The auditory pathway. Diagram of the nerve pathway from the cochlea (inner ear) to the cortex of the brain.
(*Reproduced with permission from 'Hearing in Man and Animals',*
R. T. Beatty, Bell, London.)

inhibitory process develops. By the age of 6 to 8 months a loud sound evokes only a slight movement of the eyes, not necessarily towards the source of the sound, or there may be a momentary cessation of movement. Repetition of the sound usually produces no response at all. There is a danger here in the testing of hearing because it may be thought that the response to the first presentation of the sound was just a fluke; as a result unwarranted suspicions of deafness may arise and cause great concern.

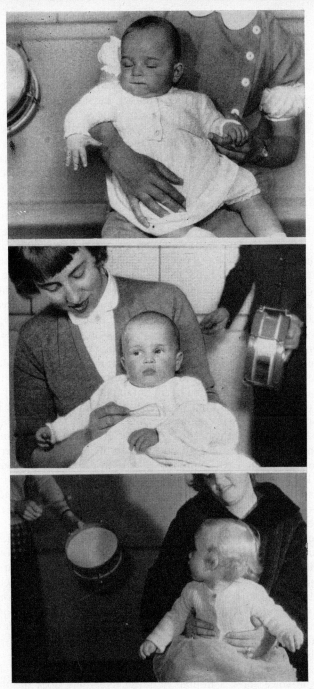

Figure III.4. Babies with normal hearing: response to loud sounds (drum):

(*a*) 3½ months: the baby blinks and gives a little jerk.

(*b*) 7½ months: inhibition of the startle response has begun. A loud sound elicits only a slight movement of the eyes, not necessarily towards the source of the sound.

(*c*) 8½ months: the startle response has been replaced by a learnt response. The infant turns and localises the source of the sound.

(*Reproduced from 'The Deaf Child', Edith Whetnall and D. B. Fry.*
William Heinemann Medical Books, London.)

It must be emphasised that the ages given are average ages. There may be great variations in the speed with which inhibition develops. Almost complete inhibition of the startle reflex has been seen in an infant of 3 months. The parents were worried because their child failed to respond to loud sounds. In fact this child was already beginning to localise faint sounds and could imitate the sound made by striking a bar on the xylophone. He had normal hearing.

Between the 8th and 10th month the startle reflex is replaced by a new response. The infant turns and localises the source of the sound. This ability to localise is something that the infant has been gradually learning as a response to quieter sounds, which in the first three months elicit very little response. The first response to a quiet sound is for the infant to keep quite still for a few seconds. This has been seen as early as three weeks. By seven weeks there is an attempt to lift the head. After about three months there is a difference in the response, depending on whether the quiet sound is new and unfamiliar or not. Familiar sounds are really 'learnt' sounds and the changed response to familiar sounds is the first positive evidence of 'learning to hear'. The inhibition of the startle response is the negative side of this learning process.

The development of this new response coincides with the infant's development of the ability to lift and turn the head. The infant of 3 to 8 months confronted by an unfamiliar quiet sound will look once towards the sound but with repetition of the sound there is no response. Here again is a danger for the tester of hearing who is not fully conversant with normal responses. If each new sound is presented first to the right ear and then to the left, the observer will note a response to each sound from the right ear and none from the left. He may draw the wrong conclusion that the infant is deaf in the left ear. If the first new sound is presented to the right ear and the second sound to the left ear and so on, alternately, this mistake will not be made.

The response to sounds which have become familiar is different. The infant turns his head sharply and looks at the source of the sound. The number of sounds which have become familiar will depend on the infant's experience and so will the order in which the sounds are learnt. It is obvious that sounds which have been heard often will be more familiar and that sounds which have an important meaning for the child will be the most easily learnt. Sounds connected with feeding are very important, such as the tap of a spoon on a bottle or cup (Figure III.5).

Most important of all is the sound of the mother's voice. Tests with the voice show a double response. Not only does the infant turn and localise the source of the sound. He may also be induced to use his own voice, attempting to imitate the sounds he hears

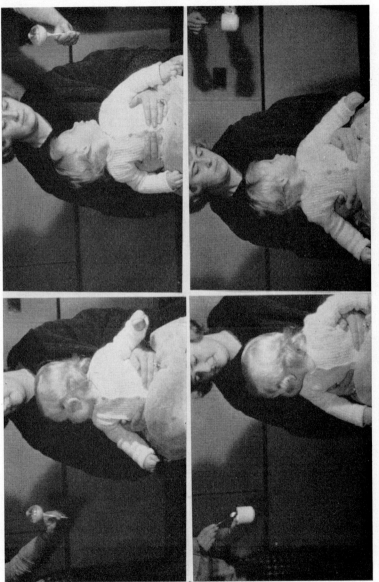

Figure III.5. Infant (8½ months) with normal hearing. She has learnt the meaning of many sounds. She turns and looks at the source of quiet, familiar sounds—high pitch rattle and cup tapped with a spoon. (*Reproduced from 'The Deaf Child', Edith Whetnall and D. B. Fry. William Heinemann Medical Books, London.*)

(Figure III.6). By the age of 6 months normal patterns of intonation of phrases and vowel sounds can be recognised in the sounds the baby makes. Tervoort reported an interesting study of 'babbling'—

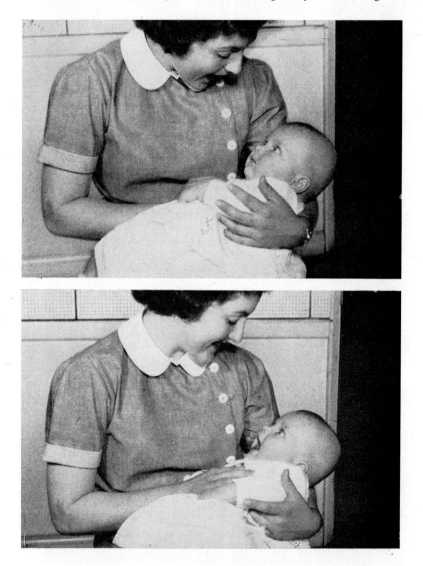

Figure III.6. Infant (6½ months) with normal hearing: response to the voice by imitation.
(*Reproduced from 'The Deaf Child', Edith Whetnall and D. B. Fry. William Heinemann Medical Books, London.*)

the vocal sounds made by babies. He made recordings of the babbling of Dutch babies, English babies and one Chinese baby who had not heard any language other than Chinese. He had his students listen to the recordings and asked them if they could tell from the babble whether the babies had been exposed to the sounds of the students' own language or to a foreign language. With a baby of four to five months old the students could not distinguish the foreign babies. By 9 months the babbling of a Dutch child sounded 'foreign' to English people. The child is beginning to reproduce the sounds he hears around him and this reproduction is based on the preceding months of listening and learning to discriminate. The child has been 'learning to hear' and is on the way to the acquisition of 'comprehension hearing'.

The reader may feel that a good deal of the description given above is rather artificial, but the tests of hearing which have been mentioned are probes with which the otologist, psychologist or other tester can sample the learning process in the infant. This has two purposes—the acquisition of knowledge about the learning process in general, and the testing of a particular infant's progress along the path of learning. It is a truism that the infant's early years are full of learning. More learning is packed into the three years between birth and the child's third birthday than will ever be packed into the three years that separate the University freshman from the Bachelor of Arts or Science. The child acquires all sorts of motor skills, but he also acquires an immense amount of information. This information comes largely through the special senses of sight, touch, taste, smell and hearing. We have seen that hearing is the latest comer of these special senses. Its operation is largely unseen. This is one of the great difficulties about understanding the process of learning to hear and this in its turn leads to the difficulties of helping the child with impaired hearing. We see the infant grasp an object, look at it, put it in his mouth, smell it, and we realise that he is learning how that object feels, looks, tastes and smells. We do not so easily realise that all the time he is also learning the meaning of sounds.

At first all sounds are without meaning. Think how meaningless are the sounds of a foreign language to an adult who has not learnt that particular language (Figure III.7). The baby's native language is just as meaningless to him as any foreign language. Indeed it has less meaning than the foreign language has for an adult. At least the adult knows that these curious noises are a 'language'. The baby has no idea what a language is. He has to learn that the noises coming from other people have a meaning and that by producing similar noises he can influence what other people do. Go back a stage in imagination. Think of the noises in an unfamiliar house or district, the unfamiliar out-of-door noises when the town dweller visits the country especially if he is camping. The strange unfamiliar noises are at first quite mystifying, mysterious, even sinister. Every sound is unfamiliar to the baby. As he lies there in his cot or pram he has to sort them out and attach them to their different meanings.

Figure III.7. The British Character, Skill at Foreign Languages.
(*Pont (1942). Collins, London (by kind permission).*)

Parents are impatient for their child to produce his first word. The miracle is that he should learn so much about sound in so short a time. This miracle depends on the one great advantage the infant has over the adult: in infancy there is a special facility to learn—to learn everything, including speech.

Although the development of hearing is largely a hidden process the progressive development of more obvious skills is well known. Paediatricians talk of the normal 'milestones' of development, babbling, sitting up, crawling, walking. Although there are individual variations in the times at which these milestones occur, there is a general pattern of development which all normal babies follow. This development may be influenced by environment but even more important is the *maturation* of the nervous system. Without maturation learning can not take place and maturation seems to depend on myelination. A fully developed nerve fibre is surrounded by a sheath made of a substance called 'myelin'. Fibres in different pathways or 'tracts' of the nervous system receive their myelin sheaths at different times. This is important because it is generally believed that nerve fibres are incapable of conducting impulses until they have acquired their myelin sheaths—until they are 'myelinated'. One explanation of this is that the sheath acts as an insulator to confine the nerve impulse to an individual fibre and prevent its interaction with neighbouring fibres. Sensory fibres are myelinated before motor fibres. The first fibres in the cerebral hemispheres to become myelinated are the sensory fibres passing to the 'somaesthetic' parts of the cortex, i.e. the areas dealing with touch and with kinaesthetic or proprioceptive sensation—the sensation that tells us about movements of muscles and other parts of our bodies. This begins in the embryo in the eighth month of intrauterine life. Next come the sensory fibres leading to the visual and the auditory cortex. Myelination of the motor fibres passing from the motor cortex to the muscles commences in the second month after birth and is not complete until the second year. It follows that all movements and responses made by the infant in the first two months are reflex, depending on the spinal cord and the brain stem and not involving the cerebral cortex. This is why the early responses to sound are reflex. The gradual inhibition of these reflex responses is dependent on increased control by the cerebral cortex and this in turn is dependent on the myelination of the cerebro-spinal or motor tracts. The so-called 'psychic' areas of the cortex and the association fibres acquire their myelin sheaths even later.

Not only is it impossible for new behaviour to take place until the appropriate tracts are myelinated but there seems to be a special facility for acquiring new forms of behaviour while myelination is going on. This would explain the *special facility to learn* in the first two or three years of life. What is, however, certain, and more practically important, is that this increased facility exists. The corollary is that learning becomes increasingly difficult if, for any reason, it is prevented in the important early years.

Some of the 'milestones' of development depend almost entirely on the processes of myelination and maturation which are taking place in the baby's central nervous system. For others it is necessary, in addition, for the correct conditions to be present in the environment. This is particularly true of the development of hearing and speech. The child in a normal home is surrounded by sounds that have meaning. The most important of these are connected with his mother and with feeding. He will spend long hours sleeping quietly in his pram but each time he is fed, bathed or changed he will be lapped round by waves of sound and, most importantly, of speech sounds. We have described the baby's early reflex responses to sound. Confronted with a baby, adults and older children have what seems almost to be a reflex urge to address the infant. He is, after all, the best captive audience in the world, and it is really quite comical to observe even taciturn people with a baby and see how they chatter away. A similar 'reflex' makes people talk to cats and dogs but this does not lead to talking cats and dogs. The development of speech depends on the interaction of the environment and of processes going on inside the human baby's brain.

Kerr Love, an ear specialist interested in deaf children half a century ago, counted the number of words used to a baby in half an hour—the total was 305. The young baby is very appealing so the speech that surrounds him will usually be in a pleasant tone of voice. Often the speech will be accompanied by the pleasant sensation of being fed. All of this must aid the learning of the meaning of sound. One of the early discriminations the baby learns to make is between a pleased and a displeased tone of voice. Gradually he learns to make finer and finer discriminations. He begins to respond to speech by making vocal noises himself, and receives a further stimulus to the understanding and production of sound from the pleased expression of his mother or the other adults around him.

Much of our knowledge about the normal functioning of the body comes from observing the effects of disease or other abnormal conditions. The study of patients with strokes has told neurologists much about the normal activity of the brain and other parts of the central nervous system. A study of *infants deprived of sound* throws light on the normal learning of hearing or speech. This deprivation of sound may sometimes occur in a residential nursery when the staff does not have sufficient time to give the children individual attention or it may occur in a neglected home.

In the course of Pavlov's experiments on conditioned reflexes he tried the effect of presenting the new learnt 'conditioned' stimulus again and again without reinforcement, i.e. he did not 'reinforce' the new stimulus by occasionally giving food along with it. The effect of this was to inhibit the conditioned response. In the same way, children who do not receive any incentive associated with sound— no noises connected with preparation of the feed, no affectionate voice while being fed—these children not only fail to learn to hear but their response to sound is inhibited and they almost learn not to hear.

These sound-deprived children appear to be even deafer than the deaf child. When they are first brought to a clinic for testing they may show absolutely no response to sound. With individual attention and an environment in which sounds are associated with meaning these children will learn to hear and will eventually be found to have normal hearing.

It should be noted that this deprivation of sound is not necessarily due to any vicious neglect on the part of the adults caring for the child. Sometimes it arises from an erroneous suspicion of deafness. The parents stop talking to the child because they feel it is useless.

RBN has a vivid recollection of such a child seen by EW—a doctor's child who was born prematurely and spent the first four months of his life in an oxygen tent. The parents were correctly warned that there was a risk of such a child being deaf. They were not advised what to do about it. At the age of 8 months the child was still very behind in babbling and did not appear to respond to sound. The parents made frequent tests of hearing. No reward was associated with the loud sounds they used in testing so that any response the child might have had was inhibited. The parents became even more certain that their child was deaf and stopped speaking to him. He was seen by EW when he was 21 months old. His learning process was by now very retarded; he produced only vowel sounds and the intonation patterns of speech of a child a year younger. But on testing he responded well to faint sounds, turning and localising them on every occasion from a distance of several feet. Loud sounds were completely ignored.

EW was quite sure that the child was not deaf. She advised the parents to treat him as a normal child and to talk to him. She gave them a follow-up appointment in three months' time, not because she was in any doubt about the result, but because she did not want the parents to feel stranded. RBN answered the telephone when they rang up to cancel the appointment. "Our child is talking and it is obviously unnecessary to waste Miss Whetnall's time. We are very grateful."

EFFECTS OF DEAFNESS ON LEARNING TO HEAR

Any reader who is the parent of a deaf child may be thinking "What has all this to do with my child?" We must now consider the effects of deafness on the process of learning to hear. It depends partly on the *degree* of deafness or, put another way, on the degree of impairment of hearing. The first point to get clear is that total deafness, complete inability to hear any sound at all, is extremely rare, perhaps non-existent, in deaf-born children. EW, in an experience of several thousand children, was not convinced that she had ever seen a child born totally deaf. Some appeared to be totally deaf when first tested but after auditory training they were found to have some islands of hearing, so-called 'residual' hearing.

The almost universal existence of some residual hearing is of the first importance. Another very important fact follows from the earlier part of this chapter. We must remember the necessity for even the 'normally hearing child' to 'learn to hear'. Although much neglected, this is not a new idea. As long ago as 1911 Kerr Love was writing:—

"But none of the special senses is automatic at birth; all have to be trained before they become automatic. All children are born deaf and blind."

The difficulty of the deaf child comes from the fact that the cortical centres in the brain are dependent on the information that reaches them as nerve impulses from the peripheral sense organs. Like computers they cannot function if no information is fed into them and they cannot function adequately with inadequate information. With a minor degree of hearing impairment the cortical centres may receive enough auditory information for the infant to 'learn to hear' without a great deal of difficulty. The process will be a little delayed and the production of speech may be imperfect, but no baby's speech is perfect and the partial hearing loss may not be detected until the child reaches school and even later.

With greater degrees of hearing impairment, difficulties are obviously greater until we reach the level at which the child's cortex receives so little auditory information that the child does not even learn that sound has any meaning at all. Such a child cannot develop speech 'spontaneously'. Some extra help is needed. Sound must be amplified so that the centres in the brain have the stimuli necessary for the process of learning to take place.

The mothers of the deaf children with 'spontaneous' speech described in the previous chapter had provided this amplification by drawing the child close and speaking into his or her ear. A hearing aid is even better. This enables the baby to be constantly in an environment of sound, not just when the mother is talking into the ear. It also means that the baby can look at the mother while she is speaking and so associate the sounds with the expression on the mother's face and with her lip and mouth movements. EW put aids on younger and younger children and found that the earlier they had their aids the better they did.

CONDITIONS FOR LEARNING TO HEAR

Early on in the development of the auditory method, EW formulated certain conditions which had to be present if a baby was to learn to hear and to develop comprehension hearing. These conditions had to be satisfied whether the peripheral mechanism of hearing was normal or impaired. The difference is that with a normal peripheral hearing mechanism and an average home environment the conditions are automatically present; with an impaired peripheral hearing mechanism special steps have to be taken to provide these essential conditions. This list of conditions summarises what has been said in previous pages.

If the baby is to learn to hear he must be supplied with *sounds*:—

loud enough;

often enough;

at the right *early* age of facility to learn;

in a *hearing environment* where individual attention can be given to help him to associate sounds and especially words with their meanings and where there is affection and an incentive to learning.

The deaf child's chance to develop his residual hearing and to achieve speech through comprehension hearing depends on the extent to which the adults round him supply these essential conditions.

CHAPTER IV

DEAF BUT NOT DUMB

If you are concerned with bringing up a child who is deaf, either through being born with a hearing loss or having suffered it at an early age, you are facing a problem and nowhere in this book have we tried to give any other impression. What we are trying to do is to show as clearly as we can where this problem lies, because this is not quite where people often think, and to point out where the real solution is to be found.

There is a quite fundamental reason why the deaf child should present such a problem and that is that our basic way of communicating with each other, as human beings, is by means of sounds. Millions of words have been written over the centuries about the nature of man, what he really is, from *homo sapiens* through the computer on legs to the 'naked ape'; but when we come right down to it, what man is above all is a talking animal. In the course of our history we have developed an acoustic, auditory way of making contact with our fellow men and since without this contact a man is not in any real sense a man, the capacity for speech lies at the very heart of our lives.

Try to imagine for a moment that our history had taken a different turn. Our eyes and our vision play an enormously important part in our daily lives and so we might perhaps have developed a visual system of communication instead of an auditory one. In that case we should spend a great deal of our time tick-tacking or semaphoring to each other and our facial expressions would play an even greater role in communication than they do at present. Most important of all, from our point of view, the situation of the child born deaf and the child born blind would be completely reversed. The deaf child would easily and happily develop the common means of communication in the normal way and the blind child would be handicapped by the great obstacle standing in the way of his acquiring the normal method of making contact with other people. As things are, however, this problem of communication is the one that faces the parent of the deaf child. How can we best help such a child to learn to make real contact with the world around him?

This question means above all how can we teach him to speak and to take in speech, for there is no effective substitute for speech in the world of human relationships. In this chapter we shall try to put in front of you some basic ideas about the way in which speech works and to show the reasons why the position of the deaf child, in this respect, is by no means as hopeless as it would first appear. Admittedly speech communication is a matter of sounds passing between people and we are talking about a child who cannot hear sounds or cannot hear them very well, so there would be every justification for thinking, as unfortunately so many people have thought over the years, that for the deaf child to acquire speech is impossible. This is just not true and there are hundreds of children and grown-ups now walking about who actively demonstrate the opposite. Why this should be so we shall explain in detail in the following pages, but there are briefly two reasons for it; the first is that speech communication depends very much less on sounds and on the ear than we believe, the second is that the sounds we do need to hear in speech do not have to be of the high quality that we generally imagine is necessary.

Speech and Language

There is a certain difficulty in writing about speech in that a good deal of the time we are in fact discussing sounds but there is not, at least as yet, any way in which the reader can hear sounds off the printed page. There are, however, quite a number of parallels between hearing and seeing, especially where language is concerned, so we shall make use of this fact in putting forward some of the basic ideas.

First of all, look carefully at the following lines of print.

Bu kitabı okuyan sizler sağu olabilirsiniz; işitme kabiliyetiniz geçmişe nazaran azalmış olabilir veyahut aileden veya arkadaşlardan işitme kabiliyeti az olan kimseler hususi dersler alarak kendilerini karşısındakilere tanıtıp karşısındakileri anlıyabilir.

If you live permanently in England, the chances that you can understand what this says are very small indeed. But of course you can see it perfectly clearly and you may notice a number of details about the way it is printed—that sometimes the letters s and c appear with a cedilla, ş and ç, and sometimes not; the letter i may be dotted or not, i and ı, and g turns up with and without an accent, ğ and g. It is clear that your being unable to understand it is not something connected with your eyes or your vision. You will probably say at this point, and perhaps rather impatiently, "Of course it's because I don't know the language!" That is very true, and what this underlines for us is that "knowing a language" is very largely a matter for the brain, not for the eye or the ear; to know a language means to carry round an enormous store of information of a particular kind in your head.

Now someone might come along and read that same passage aloud to you (it is in Turkish). In that case your ears would hear a stream of sounds and might notice quite a lot of things about those sounds, but again you would be unable to understand what was said because you do not know the language. There is nothing wrong with your hearing but you have never had the opportunity to collect in your brain all the information needed in order to 'know Turkish'. This shows us that learning a language is primarily a matter of training the brain, of giving it the chance to amass a vast store of information which it can call upon whenever a spoken or written message needs to be understood.

A child who is born with a hearing loss is not born with a 'brain loss'; there is every chance that his brain will function just as well as any other child's and this means that the absolutely vital part of the speech and language learning apparatus is intact. What we have established so far, however, is only that perfect hearing (or perfect sight) is not enough to enable us to understand. What if we have less than perfect hearing or sight? Doesn't this make matters much worse?

Look now at the next line of print:

It is certainly not difficult to read this line of print.

Here your eye is being provided with only about half of each letter and yet reading the sentence probably gives you no trouble at all. First and foremost this is because you know English, your brain has all the knowledge necessary for understanding an English sentence. In these circumstances it is not too important that your eye is being deprived of nearly half the information it would normally receive; your brain is quite capable of guessing what the missing half is and so of reading the message. As a matter of fact, this is the way in which we generally deal with messages, whether they are spoken or written. The printed example given above is of course an unusual one, but in speech it is not so uncommon as you might suppose for a good deal of the sound information to be missing. Every time you use an ordinary telephone you are coping with speech from which a considerable proportion of the acoustic information has been subtracted. We are able to use the system without difficulty— most of the time, at least—simply because the brain is very good at guessing. When a proper name or an uncommon word turns up in a telephone conversation we may well be temporarily stumped but our ability to guess is soon restored. Supposing one person says: "Oh, by the way, I saw old Haythornthwait yesterday," the other is most likely to say: "Who?" and to ask for repetitions until the first speaker begins to spell out the name: "H for Harry, A for apple, Y for York, T for Tommy, H for Harry, O for orange, R for Robert . . .". At this point the second person is very likely to exclaim: "Oh, you mean Haythornthwait." What he means is of course' "I can guess the rest, so don't bother to spell out any more."

This ability to guess what is coming next lies behind all our use of language. We apply it the whole time, whether we are taking in speech, print or handwriting. Most people are well aware that when we are reading we do not look at separate letters, we can judge what a word is by the general outline. In a rather similar way, we do not need to hear every sound a speaker makes in order to recognise what he has said; if we hear about half of it, we can fill in the rest from our knowledge of what it must be. A very effective method of demonstrating our capacity in this direction was devised by Claude Shannon, one of the originators of communication theory, and it is a method which anyone can try out so long as he can find an acquaintance patient enough to act as his guinea-pig. You first of all select a printed sentence from a newspaper, preferably one your friend has not yet read. Without telling him anything at all about the sentence, you then set him to guessing one after the other what the letters are that make up the sentence. He starts off with the first letter in the sentence; there are only 26 letters in the alphabet and of course you encourage him not to repeat any letters when he is guessing at each position, if necessary keeping a record of the actual guesses. Each time he is wrong, you tell him so and stop him when he guesses the correct letter for the first position in the sentence. He then starts guessing all over again for the second letter, and so on through the sentence. The important thing is that you make a note of how many guesses he needed at each position. Even at the first position he is very unlikely to need all 26 guesses, for after all there are some letters which are very unlikely to occur in the first place, letters like x, z, or q for example. You will find however that as he proceeds through the sentence he will need fewer and fewer guesses, generally speaking, and towards the end he will be guessing quite a proportion of the letters with his first guess.

The same effect can be shown with regard to the sounds of the language. In Figure IV.1.– you can see the result of one such guessing game in which an English person was asked to guess the sequence of sound units, or phonemes, in the sentence *My brother's just bought a new house*. The height of each rectangle in the figure shows the number of guesses he needed before hitting on the correct sound at each position. We are here concerned with the sound units of the language and not with ordinary letters, and as we shall see later on, the total number of different sounds that may occur is just over 40 compared with the 26 letters of the printed language. For this reason the maximum number of guesses possible is greater than in the case of the ordinary spelling of the sentence. A transcription of the sequence of sound units or phonemes is shown below the rectangles, with the orthography beneath. At the first position, the person guessing required 20 guesses before he suggested *m*, but at once something interesting happens because he then suggests the next sound correctly with his first guess. You will no doubt feel

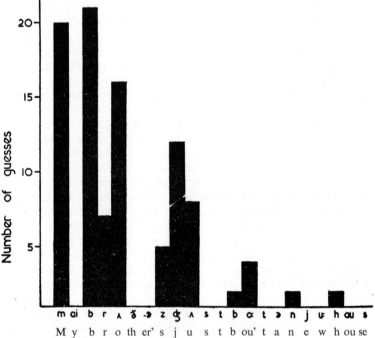

Figure IV.1. The result of an experiment that demonstrates the linguistic knowledge accessible to the listener. The figure shows the number of guesses required by a subject in guessing successively the phonemes in the sentence "My brother's just bought a new house".

inclined to comment at once that this is simply because he has thought of the word *my*. This is perfectly correct and expresses the main point of what is being demonstrated here—that to know an English word means to know what sounds occur in it and in what order. When a fresh word begins, there is an increase in the number of guesses needed; for the word *brother*, the number rises to 21, for *just*, to 12. The most striking effect, though, is that the general level of the number of guesses falls very rapidly as the sentence proceeds until towards the end of it nearly every sound is correct at the first guess; a second guess is needed only when there are fresh words, *new* and *house*. Of course we are giving him a lot of information by telling him when he guesses wrongly, but remember that the person guessing does not *hear* any of the sounds that make up the sentence;

he simply draws all the information about what is going to happen out of his own brain. The whole sentence is composed of 22 sound units and it happens that he gets 11 of these at the first guess.

One important fact that has come out of studying English by this technique is that vowel sounds are more easily guessed than the consonant sounds. This means that vowels actually supply us with less information than consonants—we can do without them more easily, as we can show even by examples in ordinary spelling. In the line below, all the vowel letters have been omitted, but you will find very little difficulty in knowing what the words are:

M-r- h-d - l-ttl- l-mb

and yet in the next one, where all the consonant letters are omitted, it will probably take you quite a few seconds to decide what is being said:

O-e --e -i--- a-- -a- a-ay

This difference in predictability between vowels and consonants will turn out later to be very relevant to the problem of the deaf child and his learning to hear and speak. For the moment the significant fact is that everyone who knows English is very clever at guessing what is coming next in any message spoken in English.

All languages, whether in their spoken or written form, share this feature which is called 'redundancy'. Technically the term refers to the fact that at any point in a message what comes next is to a greater or less degree predictable but we can usefully apply the word in its more everyday sense to speech to mean that any message contains more information than we strictly need to understand it. This is the main reason why speech as a means of communication is so successful. It may at first seem surprising that it should be considered in this light since we normally notice only the occasions when things go wrong in speech—when people fail to understand what is said, or ask questions or want repetitions. The fact is, however, that by far the greater part of speech passes between speaker and listener without any difficulty whatever and this is due to the redundancy of languages. One can say that in speech there is always a great 'safety margin' which serves to safeguard the meaning of the message, even in the face of very difficult conditions. One difficulty which is ever present is the fact that no two individuals speak alike. Not only do people from different parts of the British Isles and different parts of the world speak different kinds of English, but even within these variations, there are individual differences in voice and pronunciation. Were it not for our well-developed capacity for guessing, we should quite frequently find it impossible to know what people are saying to us even in our own language. As it is, a breakdown of this kind is a very rare occurrence.

There is a good parallel here between speech and handwriting, for everyone has his own writing as well as his own speech. We are often aware when reading handwriting that we have simply to guess many words or even phrases which we should be incapable of deciphering letter by letter but we do not realise how very frequently we are doing the same thing in receiving speech. Errors do sometimes occur in speech. Often they are spotted by the speaker who breaks off and corrects himself or they are corrected mentally by the listener. It is quite possible for them to go unnoticed by either, particularly when the degree of redundancy is such that there can be no doubt what the message is meant to be. This can be demonstrated easily by making 'deliberate mistakes'. Try in a suitable situation asking a waiter or your neighbour at table for a 'tlean dlass' instead of a 'clean glass' and it is most unlikely that anyone but yourself will be aware that anything unusual has happened.

The factor of redundancy must clearly have a great bearing on our problem since it represents a means through which lack of acoustic information can be compensated for. Deafness certainly constitutes a reduction in the available acoustic information, but if we can in some way make sure that the deaf child learns his mother tongue as thoroughly as the normally hearing child, he will then be in a position to benefit from the redundancy of the language, to guess just as effectively as anyone else and to make sense of what he hears in spite of his hearing loss. More than this, if his own speech is not quite like the majority of people's, he will still be understood, provided he reaches a certain level of naturalness, because his listeners will exercise their own ability to guess.

We must now look in more detail at what happens in speech in order to see how and why it is possible to achieve this state of affairs. The best way to do this is perhaps to follow the stages by which the normally hearing child learns to talk and acquires his own language and to ask at each step whether a deaf child can be brought to the same state and if so, how?

Baby Sounds and Babbling

Why do babies cry? Any mother can answer this question very readily. They cry because they are uncomfortable in some way—they are hungry, or they have a pain, or have been suddenly disturbed or need changing. So the baby gives tongue in a cry which does not vary so very much in a particular baby. At first, so long as the baby is quite comfortable he will not make any sound but after some weeks he begins to make sounds when he is particularly pleased with life as well as when things are going wrong. The two kinds of sound are very different from each other. A mother, especially with her first baby, often finds the cry rather distressing, even after she has learned to regard it mainly as a signal to herself to 'do something about it', but the cooing which the baby is generally giving by the time it is three months old is often what makes everything else worthwhile.

Though there is so much difference in character between the loud, insistent sound of the cry and the much gentler, more intermittent comfort sounds, in both cases the baby is using already much of the mechanism that will later enable him to talk, his breathing muscles, his voice-box or larynx and his tongue and lips. When he is lying peacefully in his cot, we can hear his breathing as a regular rhythmical 'in-out'; when he begins to cry, this is all changed. Sometimes a single cry goes on and on until one wonders how he can keep it up without bursting, then there is a short break while he takes in more air, just in order to start all over again. Only the air coming *from* the lungs is used to make the sound, just as it is in speech. In fact some of our more talkative acquaintances are not unlike the crying baby, for as we sometimes say 'they pause only to draw breath'.

During this time the baby is not only sending out sounds, he is beginning to notice the sounds around him. He will soon begin to associate his mother's voice with very pleasant things like feeding and bathing and after a short while he reacts to the voice itself, especially to the tone of voice, and he will smile simply in response to it. Even at this early stage, it is important for the baby to be talked to a great deal because this is what develops his capacity for listening. But the talking has to be linked with things that interest the baby and so the mother instinctively talks to him while she is feeding, bathing and dressing him. When this happens the child very soon cottons on to the fact that speech is connected in a rather special way with his world and this is a vital step in the process by which, when the time comes, he becomes ready to talk.

Generally in the period from about four to nine months of age the baby enters on a stage which is of the utmost importance for learning to talk and which we call 'babbling'. This is the time when, on waking in the morning and before going to sleep, and indeed at almost any time when he is alone, he will be making streams of sounds, of one kind and another, repeating syllables over and over again, stringing them together and in fact 'playing at talking'. We have only to eavesdrop on this activity for a few seconds to be convinced that the baby is having fun; he is now getting real pleasure just from uttering sounds, without any reference to the world around him. A number of developments are taking place at this time and in order to understand their importance we need to know something more about the way in which we all control our muscles when we are talking.

We all of us, however modest, like to hear ourselves talk, not in the sense in which we sometimes say of someone 'He loves the sound of his own voice', but in the sense that, if we have to talk, we prefer to be able to hear ourselves. When we go into some particularly noisy place, we often say 'You can't hear yourself talk' or sometimes even 'You can't hear yourself think', which is an interesting sidelight on the extent to which we identify thinking with speech. This need to hear ourselves when we are talking is so fundamental that we quite unconsciously adapt the volume of our speech to any noise that may surround us; the louder the noise, the louder we talk. This is why being at a party can sometimes be so tiring. Any considerable number of people talking at once will make a high level of noise and every individual who is talking will raise his voice to try and overcome this, and so the amount of noise increases and increases. In these circumstances, by the way, we always believe that we are talking loudly so that the person we are talking to should be able to hear, but really the main reason for it is that we need to hear ourselves.

You may think that this connection between speaking and hearing is quite obvious but in fact it works in very subtle and complicated ways, of which we are quite unaware. When we are talking, the sounds which come from our mouths are set up by the movements of a great many muscles, muscles in the face, the mouth, the throat, the larynx, the chest. It is the brain which controls these immensely complicated actions by sending instructions to all the muscles telling them what to do and the precise moment at which to do it. In order to arrange the programme of instructions and to see that it is effectively and smoothly carried out, the brain needs to receive information continuously from the ears, that is the speaker's ears, telling it what sounds have been uttered, how far the programme has got and confirming generally that the system is working properly. So it is really this requirement which lies behind a hoarse voice and a feeling of exhaustion (though not of course the hangover) after a lively party.

Let's go back now to our baby who is beginning to babble. Strange as it may seem, we had originally to learn about this connection between speaking and hearing, just as we had to learn everything we do in speech. The most important thing that is happening when the baby is at the babbling stage is exactly that: he is learning to connect up what he is doing in his mouth and his larynx with the sounds that he hears while he does it. He tries out all kinds of movements and discovers what sounds they produce; he repeats movements over and over again and finds, to his great satisfaction, that they make the same sound; for the sheer pleasure of it he makes rhythmical movements and finds that they produce rhythmical sounds.

After a few weeks of babbling a baby will generally have quite a wide repertory of different sounds, some of which sound very strange to the mother. He is really exploring the possibilities of the talking-box that nature has provided him with and is intent on finding out all the curious and exciting things that can be done with it. Many of the sounds he makes will be very useful later on when he begins to string them together into English words; some of them will be discarded because they have no place in English. In both cases a very important job is being done because at one and the same time the baby is learning habits of movement and, through his brain, linking up his muscles with his ears. He is beginning to build up an enormous capital of knowledge about speech which he will keep in his memory and will draw upon for the rest of his life. Habitual movements are the basis of so much that we do in daily life, from brushing our teeth to driving a car, and acquiring them for speech is a vital part of learning to talk. Babbling is in some ways rather like the early stages of learning to play the piano; a child will spend many hours learning to play five-finger exercises and scales, perhaps, so that later he may be able to play a Chopin study or a Beethoven sonata. This music may well contain snatches of those very exercises and scales, but the real importance of them is that they lay the foundations of a technique, that is to say habits of movement, which will adapt itself to whatever demands may be made upon it.

One more interesting and important fact about babbling is that after a while the baby may be triggered off to start babbling by the sound of his mother's voice. This is a sign that the links between sound and movement are beginning to be established. The sound, even though it comes from another person, is enough to set the babbling off, but of course the baby goes on with his own repertory of sounds; he is not yet actively imitating sounds made to him. In fact when this does happen, it is a sign that he is beginning to move out of the babbling stage.

In a baby's development of speech, as in all his other developments, there is a good deal of variation between one child and another as to the rate at which things happen and the age at which any stage is reached, so that it is not always particularly helpful to say the 'average child' will be doing such and such at this or that age. For one thing it is generally very hard for mothers to appreciate that the 'average child' is not a real live baby, but simply a statistical figment; it is the label which is stuck on a set of numbers. However, perhaps we ought to take the risk and say that by about the age of four months your baby is very likely to be cooing and gurgling or chuckling, between six and nine months he will probably be babbling and at about nine or ten months he will be moving into the next stage, which we have not yet talked about. Before doing so, we must now go back, as we promised earlier, to see how the deaf baby will be faring up to this point.

Deaf Babies Babble

From other chapters in this book you will begin to discover what close observation, what a great deal of attention and experience is needed in order to find out with any certainty whether a baby is deaf or not. This does mean unfortunately that in many cases a mother will not realise that her baby is deaf and so he may be deprived of the help and the special care which would make a world of difference to him in later life. But it does also mean that in the earliest stages there are no very obvious differences between the behaviour of the hearing and the deaf baby. It is vital to discover at the first possible moment that a child has a hearing loss, and to do this we have to be able to notice the more subtle and much less obvious signs of something wrong, but it is at least something to know that for just the first few months of his life, the baby will begin to develop the activities that lead to speech even though he has a hearing loss.

The deaf baby, like the hearing one, begins by just crying when he is uncomfortable and there is nothing to distinguish his cry from any other. Then some time later he too will begin to coo and to gurgle with pleasure, making all the sounds that we hear at this stage from a hearing baby. We must realise of course that these are simply a natural expression of his reaction to what he is feeling at a particular moment and they are in any case not connected with hearing. However, the process continues still further, for the deaf baby will go on to the babbling stage and like the hearing baby, will soon be trying out a variety of sounds with repetitions and rhythmical sequences, in other words collecting the raw materials for speech.

He has now reached the point at which hearing is going to play an important part in his development and inevitably the degree of hearing loss from which he suffers is bound to influence the course of events materially. It is by no means easy to find out how much of his own voice a baby is able to hear but it is certain that a very severe hearing loss would have to be present to prevent him from hearing anything at all of his own cry. Nevertheless, as we have just said, the really vital part of the babbling stage is the setting up of the links between movements and sounds and there is no doubt that for this purpose the better the baby can hear the more effectively this will be done. This is why it is so important to find out whether your baby has a hearing loss at the earliest possible moment, and if he has, to fit him with hearing aids which will make sure that the connection between making sounds and hearing them is established at the right time.

We have seen that up to this point the progress of the hearing and the deaf baby are parallel. It is when the baby begins to take special notice of the sound of other people's speech, when this sound begins to trigger off his own babbling, that the serious differences will appear. One factor that contributes to this is the fact that at just about this time the baby is beginning to become mobile; he is crawling away from his mother and so the sound of her voice will become fainter for him. Many deaf babies can hear at least something of their mother's voice while they are held in her arms and are quite close to her mouth; but sounds grow fainter very rapidly as we move further away from a speaker. We do not notice this effect ordinarily in a small room but we certainly do in a lecture hall. For the deaf baby the effect is very serious indeed, for remember that even while he is being held, mother's voice will already be rather faint, so that if he crawls even a yard or so, he will soon be out of earshot.

It is at this period that deaf babies are often noticed to stop babbling gradually; sometimes they will continue for a time, but perhaps only when they can *see* that someone is talking. So the primary need is to ensure that the baby continues to hear speech. For this reason it is vital not only that the baby should have its hearing aids but also that the mother should take great care to make quite certain that her baby is hearing as much speech as possible. She needs to talk to him really even more than she might do to a normally hearing baby since he does have a difficulty to overcome. Provided these things are done, the deaf baby will continue to develop in the normal way and will lay the foundations for talking normally later on.

It would not be true to say that if this stage is missed, a child can never develop speech; in fact quite the contrary has been demonstrated in the case of many children and even adults. It is true however that the job is made very much easier and the best results are obtained if the proper mechanism, technically called 'auditory feedback', is established at the right time. When this is done, the child is in the most favourable position to learn all the things he has to know in order to speak and understand speech, and later on to read and write, in fact to learn his own language. Before we follow both the hearing and the deaf child into these later stages of development, we must take some space to say more about what it demeans to know one's mother tongue.

What is a Language?

We started this chapter by showing that language is something that you carry round in your head. Probably the form of language with which we are most immediately familiar is *words*; since you know English you must have stored in your brain quite a large collection of English words, all filed away in a variety of ways so that they are very quickly accessible to you when they are wanted for one purpose or another. A certain proportion of them you are needing constantly for your everyday talking and these will generally 'come to mind', as we say, whenever they are required and without your being even aware that you are calling for them, except on those rare occasions when we have to stop what we are saying and say: 'The word's got away from me, but I shall think of it in a moment'. The total number of different words that you are likely to be using in ordinary speech is rather smaller than most of us believe—several thousand, perhaps four to five thousand at the most. This refers of course only to words you are likely to speak and we call this the 'active vocabulary'. Each individual speaker has an active vocabulary that is somewhat different from the next person's and we can all of us recognize and understand the words used by many different speakers. So the total number of words we can recognize is very much greater than the number we are likely to speak ourselves. Our 'passive vocabulary', as it is called, may well include a hundred or a hundred and fifty thousand words. So your brain carries in its memory store this vast collection of words; the majority of them you call on only when you are taking in speech, in order to understand what other people say to you in a very wide variety of circumstances. A comparatively small part of the stock you also call upon when you yourself are talking, in order to express what you have to say.

One thing which it is rather important for us to realise is that this 'dictionary' as we might call it really does exist in the brain of each one of us. It is not anything we pay attention to; we just use it all the time without being aware of its existence. As in the case of so many human mechanisms, we pay it attention only if something goes wrong. When elderly people suffer a stroke, it quite frequently happens that they can no longer find the words they need. This may be because the damage to the brain has actually destroyed parts of the dictionary or it may be that it has affected the part of the brain that does the looking up. In either case the person's use of language and speech is very materially affected.

A great deal of the knowledge which we need for everyday life is collected and stored without our paying it much attention and is available to us in the same way. A very rough parallel to our use of the 'dictionary' might be found in arithmetical things. If you are old enough to have learnt multiplication tables at school, for example, you have these stored away in your memory ready for use in mental arithmetic at any moment. Should you suddenly need to know what six nines are, your brain will pop up with the answer like a cash register. Notice that you certainly do not have to run through the whole six times table or anything like that, any more than you have to run through all the *d*'s in your mental dictionary to recognise the word 'dromedary'.

Our dictionary of words is only one part of the store of information on which we depend in order to use English. We have mentioned it first because it is something that we all know about; we realise that sometimes words elude us, we know that from time to time we have to learn new words like 'countdown', 'astronaut' or 'module' which we add to our passive vocabulary, at least, and perhaps to our active vocabulary. There are, however, many other vital items of information about English which we also carry in our brain. Many of these are related to the fact that words are made up of sounds. Just as any printed English word is bound to be composed of letters taken from the alphabet, so any spoken English word is made up of sound units, or 'phonemes' as such units are called. We are all very familiar with the many jokes about English spelling which are based on the discrepancies between spelling and pronunciation in English, and on the fact that English spelling does not consistently represent the sound units that occur in various words. This situation has arisen because the spelling of English words has remained relatively unchanged for a few hundred years, while the pronunciation of them has changed very considerably. The present sound system of English contains about 40 phonemes or sound units, and yet all words are spelled with the 26 letters of the alphabet. This explains why people who concern themselves either with the 'reform' of English spelling or with providing an alphabet for children who have difficulty in learning to read find that they have to design a system which contains 40 letters. We are not here concerned, of course, with spelling but we are very much concerned with the sound system of English because all those thousand of words which we carry in our brains are different arrangements of sound units or phonemes.

How can we know how many phonemes the system contains? By a very simple process of changing phonemes around in different positions. For example, all the following are quite common English words: *pin, bin, tin, din, kin, sin, fin, win*. They are different words; if we were talking and needed to use one of them, we could not simply replace it by another one since this would confuse the meaning of what we were saying. Yet the only difference between any two of these words lies in the first phoneme. We can find other examples where the only difference is perhaps in the second phoneme, as in *bit, bet, bat, but*, or in the third phoneme, as in *rip, rib, rid, rig, rim*. Of course English words may consist of much longer strings of phonemes and will generally differ from each other by more than one phoneme; they may have no phoneme in common, as in the case of the two words *stumps* and *handbag*, or they might have two in common, as in *stumps* and *humbug*, or three, like *humbug* and *handbag*, and so on. By exploring many different combinations, that is words, we eventually get to the point where our list of phonemes is complete and any fresh word we think of does not call for any phoneme that is not already counted. As we have just said, this state of affairs is reached in English with a list of about 40 phonemes. The total will differ by one or two depending on whether we are dealing with English as it is spoken in southern England or in, say, Scotland or Ireland, but in all cases the list of phonemes is substantially the same.

We are all, as speakers of English, thoroughly familiar with the system of phonemes although we are quite unaware that we have this knowledge; we know exactly what phonemes occur in the total list just as surely as we know the letters of the alphabet and we know how they can be strung together to make English words, for the language imposes some restrictions on this process. Whenever we learn a new English word, we can be sure not only that it will be made up of phonemes from the English list but that they will be combined in certain ways and not in others. It may for example contain the sequence *str*, as does indeed happen in the word 'astronaut' but it cannot for instance begin with the combination *pf* or end with *gbs*.

It may seem at first rather ludicrous to speak of all this as knowledge we carry round in our heads but this is only because we do not remember acquiring it and use it without paying it any attention. In this respect it is like many other things which we learned at an early age. In fact speech works supremely well just *because* we do it without paying attention. Imagine yourself running downstairs and think what would be the effect if you began asking yourself 'What do I do next, where do I put my foot, when do I move it?' You would most probably be in for a nasty fall. Yet we could scarcely say that you do not know how to run downstairs; it is merely that you learned this very early and you can do it smoothly so long as you do not interfere with the operation. Similarly with speech, we can take in or send out speech very successfully using a whole range of information which we acquired very early in life and provided we are prepared to leave most of the process at the automatic level where it belongs.

A knowledge of the phonemic system of our mother tongue lies at the base of all our operations with speech and language. In normal circumstances it is acquired in the first few years of life; a child will generally be familiar with the whole system by the time he is five years old and in this way will have laid the foundations for everything he will subsequently learn as part of his native language. So we must now take up again the account of the child's speech development and see how he goes on from the babbling stage to become master of the system of phonemes and of much else besides.

From Babbling to Baby-talk

You will remember that the most important aspect of babbling is that in the course of it the baby is setting up the mechanism by which he is able to control the movements of his muscles through the medium of the sounds which such movements produce. While he is learning how to do this, he is making a wide variety of sounds and using his muscles in lots of different ways. But he has not yet embarked on the use of language in any sense. What is the distinction that is being made here? We can say that language is the use of sounds deliberately to produce certain effects. It will not be so very long before our baby is making sounds that will actually produce for him delightful things like milk, cake, sweets and toys and eventually create a thousand other effects. When this begins to happen, his sounds will have become functional, they will refer in quite specific ways to his own external world and they will be used systematically—in other words, they will form a language. The first steps in this direction are connected with the system of phonemes which we have just been talking about.

We saw that English speakers operate with a system that has 40 phonemes. Of course the baby does not learn such a comparatively large and complex system all at once. What he does is to begin by building for himself a very small system which he expands gradually by incorporating new units in it. Each child is an individual and will proceed in his own way, but the earliest stages are very similar for all children. Some time during the babbling period the baby generally begins to say 'mama' when his mother appears and quite soon he will keep this word just for the occasions when he sees her. Notice that this is something new in the situation; he has certainly been making these very same sounds during his babbling but now he reserves this short sequence to refer to something outside himself, to a person in his baby world. He naturally gets a lot of help in this from his mother for she is delighted with his first steps in talking and encourages him all she can by continually repeating the word to him and by smiling and approving of his efforts. In this way the baby gets his first taste of true speech, that is speech that is operational. Perhaps at first it does no more than make his mother smile, but this means getting her attention and much more besides, so that for the baby it is establishing the basic principle that by making the right sounds he can create effects in the world around him.

Of course the baby's first word may not be 'mama' or it may not have that particular form, but it is common enough for us to take it as an example. Quite a lot of things are being crystallised with the coming of this first word, in addition to the general principle we have just mentioned. The fact that he says 'mama', duplicating the syllable, is partly the influence of the playing with sounds that has been going on during babbling; for the baby, it is more fun to say 'mama' than simply 'ma'. But at the same time, he is beginning to get the feel of the importance of syllables in speech. There will be more to say about syllables a little later, but their basic structure is already present in 'mama' through the repetition of a sequence of movements. You can easily follow these movements by saying the word slowly aloud. You begin by putting your lips together and at the same time you keep the air passage through the nose open. If this last fact is news to you, you can check the truth of it in a very simple way. Just say *m* and keep it going for a short time, and while you are doing so pinch your nose firmly between thumb and fore-finger. You will find that the sound stops abruptly, which is a good indication that it needed the air passage through the nose open. When you pass from the *m* to the *a*, you open the lips and at the same moment close up the air passage through the nose. This is done by lifting up the soft palate which is the flexible part of the roof of the mouth at the back. If you keep the *a* part of the word going and again try pinching your nose, you will find that the sound certainly does not stop, since air is coming out through the mouth only and not through the nose as it was for *m*. So these repeated syllables call for a little sequence of well-defined actions; close lips, open nose for *m*, open lips, close nose for *a*, then repeat. Although this sequence is a rather simple one, it is a very typical scheme for syllables in English.

Most important of all with this first word is the forming of a mini-system of phonemes. At present it contains only two units, *m* and *a*, so you may think it is scarcely worth calling a system, but it is one nevertheless. The two units are distinct from each other and they have to be arranged in the proper order to make the word which refers to the baby's mother. Whatever he may do when he is babbling and playing with sounds, the baby will not sometimes call her 'amam' and at other times 'mama'. The first principle of the language is already established, that the string of phonemes is closely tied to the thing that is being referred to.

This will appear more clearly if we add a second word to the first one. Very frequently this is 'dada' as a name for the baby's father. Now this system has three phonemes, the *a* which is the vowel for both words, the *m* in the first word and the *d* which is called up by the need for a second word. The scheme of syllables is the same in

the two words and since they have the same vowel, they are differentiated just by the *m* and the *d*. Perhaps the third word will be a
name for a grandparent, let us say 'baba'. This will add a fourth unit
to the system, which now consists of *a* plus *m*, *d* and *b*. Here we can
see language really at work. Notice that each fresh word comes
because it is needed, there is something for it to refer to; we do not
learn a whole lot of, as it were, 'empty' words and then look around
for things to attach them to. When the word is needed, the form for it
is found. This form consists essentially in an arrangement of phonemes and since different words have to be kept distinct from each
other we might say that the function of phonemes is to keep words
apart. This was clear earlier from the sets of words like *pin*, *tin*, *kin*,
etc., in which there was a difference in at least one phoneme. In the
baby's language we see the system in the making, for every time he
needs a new word, he adds one more phoneme to his list. It is not
absolutely necessary for him to do this; he might quite well begin
making new words by ringing the changes with the phonemes he has,
simply adopting rearrangements of them, as we do in adult language.
It is not surprising, however, that in the natural course of events the
baby prefers to add to his system because we must remember that
he has at his disposal a wide repertoire of sounds which have figured
in his babbling which can be readily pressed into service.

Perhaps at this point we ought to say a word about sounds and
phonemes. Why in all this discussion have we talked about phonemes? Wouldn't it be much easier and less confusing to call them
sounds, since that is what they seem to be? There is one technical
reason for making the distinction and that is that there are many
sound differences which do not constitute phoneme differences, but
this is not a matter which need concern us very much here. The
important point for us is the one made earlier, that processing speech
is an activity of the brain and it is the brain which deals in the classes
which we call phonemes. Speech sounds come into our ears and they
come out of our mouths in much the same way as letters are taken in
by our eyes or flow from our pen or bob up on our typewriter.
Yet you can think of the spelling of a particular word perfectly well
without visualising the letters—you hold it in your brain as some
kind of abstraction. In much the same way your brain deals with
speech, whether you are taking it in or sending it out, in the form of
abstractions which we call phonemes, which it stores, manipulates
and rearranges somewhat as though they were counters. To change
the metaphor and without wanting to imply a parallel between
computers and brains, we might say that as far as speech is concerned,
phonemes are the machine language of the brain.

The purpose of this short digression is to bring out the next
important fact about baby language and that is that the baby adds

new phonemes to his system by the process of imitating sounds which he hears from those around him and of course particularly from his mother. We said earlier that the baby's babbling is quite likely to die out if he is deprived of the stimulus of speech from other people. It is even more certain that he will not develop the system of phonemes unless he is constantly hearing speech from others. His mother's talking to him is vital not only because of the encouragement it gives him to persist in his talking but because it provides him repeatedly with patterns of sound which he imitates. In this way he learns how sounds are strung together in English and what particular arrangement of phonemes, that is what word, is used to refer to this or that object in his little world. In practice the baby learns to recognise words some time before he himself tries to reproduce them and we all know that when he does try to, his attempts at first do not sound very much like an adult's saying of the word. There is in fact that long period when 'mama' is the only person in the world who knows what he is saying! But the recognition is the important thing as far as expanding the phoneme system is concerned; the fact that the baby's own sounds are odd is less important than the fact that he is trying to make differences in the right places, is trying to reproduce the distinctions that he already hears. Of course any phoneme will not be finally established in his system until he has reached some fairly stable pronunciation of the sound concerned.

The sequence of events when a new phoneme is added, then, is approximately this: some new thing in the baby's world takes on a particular importance for him and he now notices the name for it, a new word. This word also happens to involve a new phoneme, one which has not figured in his system up to the present. For some time he just recognises this word when he hears it, but after a while he is ready to make his own attempt at saying the word and he brings it out. Perhaps the sound he makes is at first rather a long way from adult pronunciation but when she hears the word, the mother is likely to repeat it back to the baby and give him a pattern to copy. This may well have the effect of changing the baby's sound until it becomes a version which he will adopt, at any rate for the time being. Usually this is still unlike the adult sound, but it is now operative in his system; he can use it for distinguishing one word from another and he can recognise it if it turns up in yet another new word.

It is clear that expanding the phoneme system gradually until it includes all the 40 units of the adult system is going to be rather a lengthy business, but is generally pretty well complete by the time the child is four or five years old. As we have already pointed out it is a very economical way of doing things because these 40 units will provide for all the many thousands of words which the individual learns during the rest of his life. The order in which the sound units are added by the child varies a little from one child to another, but it depends largely on two things; first how common the sound is in the language, for some of them are comparatively rare, and second, how hard it is to make the required sound. Among the consonant sounds, *t* and *n* occur very commonly in English words; in 100 sounds, about 14 are likely to be either *t* or *n*. If on the other hand we take the sound that comes in the middle of words like *measure* and *leisure*, this is so rare that it crops up only once in every 1000 sounds. It also happens that *t* and *n* are relatively easy to learn for the child, so they are often the first ones to be added to the *m*, *d* and *b* that we spoke about earlier. *p* also comes quite early, and then a little later *k*, *g* and *w*. At the other end of the scale are the sounds children often find difficult, like *s*, *r* and *f*.

It is important to stress here that all this part of speech development depends on the child's continually hearing speech which it can imitate. In the ordinary way a mother will talk a great deal to her baby and thus give him the best possible chance of imitating her sounds and establishing the system of phonemes. This is absolutely essential for the hearing child and is therefore even more vital for a child who has a hearing loss. Even normally hearing children, if they are brought up in conditions where they do not hear very much speech, as sometimes happens in a residential nursery, will be noticeably backward in their speech development and especially in that vital part of it which concerns the sound system. For the baby with a hearing loss, this factor is even more important. His mother or nurse needs to talk to him even more constantly than to a hearing child and the providing of hearing aids at an early stage is essential so that he may be continually hearing the sounds which will enable him to form the basic structure of his mother tongue and to make himself understood by other people.

Generally it is the mother's speech which is the formative factor, as we can see from the fact that she not only provides the material for the system, but may often be responsible for the 'accent' which the child has. Thus one quite frequently comes across the child of, say, a Scottish mother who, in spite of living in the south and being surrounded by speakers of southern English, learns to talk with a noticeable Scottish accent. For the baby with a hearing loss, the mother's speech is a vital factor from every point of view; to give the reassurance and sense of contact which is the basis of every mother's relationship with her child, to stimulate the immensely important activity of babbling, to establish for the baby the connections between things and sounds, to give the patterns for the first words and to provide constantly models for imitation and for modifying the baby's own sounds. With the mother's interest, care and attention, and with the use of suitable hearing aids to make sure that sounds reach the baby's ears loud enough to be really used, it is possible for even a child born with a severe hearing loss to develop the system of phonemes and to be talking well by the age of four or five. When this development takes place at the right time, that is during the vital period between six months and five years of age, the most important step has been taken in overcoming the obstacle which deafness places in the way of the child's achieving normal communication with the people around him.

Words and More Words

During these early years every child, if he is given half a chance, is passionately interested in language. This is because he is discovering the whole exciting world of words, and especially because he is finding out what words will do. We all of us as grown-ups, even as parents, usually misread the significance of the child's activities in this respect. When the baby gets well into the stage of the constant: 'Wot dat?' we think that he is interested in the object referred to, although when it is the same thing for the seventy-fifth time of asking we wonder how he can keep up his interest, for he has certainly long since exhausted our own. What we do not realise is that most of the time it is not simply the object that concerns him, it is that he needs to have the *word* repeated, for the sake of the sounds it contains, to try out what it can refer to and what it can do. This function of words, their power to produce effects, is the primary reason why any child learns to talk. Perhaps this is a point at which it may be worth repeating a classic story, about the parents whose first child was, as it turned out, a rather talkative girl, who was followed at an interval of about two years by a boy. To the dismay of the parents the boy never uttered a word in his first years, and though the parents used every means to find out why this was, they were quite unable to do so; it was at least clear from other signs that the boy was not deaf. Slowly the time passed as the anxious parents saw with increasing dismay the passing of his second, third and even his fourth birthday, without his saying a word. One morning when the family were seated at breakfast he electrified the rest of them by saying loudly and distinctly: 'There's no sugar on my cornflakes'. You can imagine the mixture of delight and consternation with which his mother stammered: 'But P-P-Peter, why have you never spoken before?', to which Peter replied, rather huffily, 'Well, everything has been all right up till now!'

This puts into a nutshell why every baby wants to talk and why his major activity, apart from eating and sleeping, is words and more words. Of course we are all learning new words all the time, throughout our adult life and, as we have noted, many of these go into our passive vocabulary, fewer into our active vocabulary. In the child, too, passive and active vocabulary are growing continuously but there are changes in the rate at which they grow. At first he needs above all to have words to use, so nearly every word he learns to recognise then goes into his active vocabulary. It is quite usual to find, however, towards the middle of his second year, that there is a very rapid increase in his passive vocabulary and this is often followed by a rapid growth in the number of words used in his own speech. There is naturally already a considerable difference in size between the two vocabularies, a difference which is largely maintained for the rest of adult life.

Individual children vary a great deal in the size of their vocabulary just as they do in every other respect, so that one can give only a rough guide as to the number of words children are likely to be using at different stages. A hearing child may be using about 250 different words by the time he is two, this will grow to about 1000 by the time he is three and to 2000 when he is five. There is no reason why a child with a hearing loss, if he is given the kind of help recommended in this book, should fall materially behind a hearing child in this respect.

For the young child it is not only the number of words available which changes all the time but also the way in which words are used. Any parent who is willing to give a little attention to his child's speech can discover any number of intriguing processes that are going on. The meaning of a word can, for example, widen and contract in an astonishing manner. The most common and earliest example of this is the word 'dada'. This refers first to the strange being who may come home at the end of the day and tends to have a jolly time with the baby at the point when Mummy is out on her feet, having coped with the little angel for ten hours at a stretch. But almost invariably this stage is followed by the period when 'dada' means any figure in trousers, and perhaps a moustache, no matter when or where seen; we must all be fairly familiar with the scene in which the baby causes acute embarrassment to some perfectly strange young man by hailing him loudly as 'dada'. The meaning of the word for the child has now widened tremendously to include almost all males. Then the meaning of the word contracts once more as soon as the new word 'man' is added to the vocabulary, usually with considerable encouragement from Mummy, who is not too keen to prolong this situation.

This happens to be an example which recurs very frequently with children, but with any individual child you may come across most unlikely areas of meaning covered by a particular word in its early stages of use. One small boy, for instance, learned the word *ladder*, which he pronounced 'ladler', because of painting work on the house opposite. But 'ladler' for him meant a ladder, anything propped against the side of a house, any shape such as the back of a garden seat consisting of two arms with slats across *and* any man in white overalls. We can see here how the addition of several words will eventually narrow down the meaning of this word until it comes to mean just—a ladder. Similarly, and for the same little boy, at one period 'rain' meant not only wet stuff that fell but also *a reason for not going out*. So in perfectly fine weather when at midday it was so hot that going into the garden was not encouraged, he would go to the back door, hold his hand out and say 'rain', not as a question but as a statement meaning 'we don't go out'.

These processes are an essential part of learning one's native language and can be seen in any child, whether normally hearing or with a hearing loss. To be able to spot them gives one an insight into how things are developing in the child and is particularly helpful for the mother of a deaf child who needs to find out all she can about how speech is learned and how language is acquired. Helping a deaf child is at all times hard work and must often seem temporarily unrewarding. There are bound to be periods when a mother doubts very much whether anything at all is happening, but if she can see the kind of progress we have just been talking about, such periods may be few and far between.

Talking Grammar

We have now looked at the way in which the young child builds up his knowledge of the sound system of his native language and also at some of the things that are happening as he adds words to his vocabulary. At some time, usually between the ages of eighteen months and two years, another very significant language development takes place. This is connected with grammar. Here we are in a difficulty because for most of us, perhaps as a result of more or less painful school days, grammar means only a host of complicated rules which one is supposed to adhere to when speaking or writing and which one is continually 'breaking'. But really grammar is just a statement, in summarised form, of what people do when they talk and is not a matter of what they *should* do. Just as there are wide differences of pronunciation between dialects in England, so there can be differences in grammar. Thus a village child who was heard to call out: "''Er bain't a-calling we, us don't belong to she" was following the grammar of his dialect just as certainly as another child who might have said: "She's not calling us, we don't belong to her". Grammar deals basically with the way in which words are strung together, with what forms of words can come next to each other and which cannot, with the customs you must observe in this matter if you want to be properly understood. In English, for instance, 'Horse bites man' and 'Man bites horse' convey two very different states of affairs even though the same three words are used in both cases. If we want to be understood we cannot disregard facts of this kind about the language and of course they are facts which we all know, although fortunately we are not usually called upon to formulate them as 'rules'.

Up to the age of about eighteen or twenty months most children say one word at a time. We have seen that this single word may include a whole lot of ideas but it stands by itself. At about this period, most children begin to put two words together and this is a definite landmark in their development of speech and language, since it marks the point at which they begin to store information about the grammar. You will remember that at this stage the child is operating with a restricted phoneme system and has perhaps about a couple of hundred words at his disposal, so he is working with a little language of his own. When he begins to put two words together, he quickly develops a grammar which is suited to his little language. His words now divide themselves into two classes, each having a particular function. This is the time when the baby says things like: "Bye-bye Daddy", "bye-bye Mummy", "bye-bye sock", "bye-bye boat" and "all-gone milk", "all-gone soap", "all-gone car" and so on. Here the word that gets repeated in different combinations is a kind of operator word and it goes with the names of different things to make a kind of sentence. When this system is established, the majority of words the child uses go into the name class and comparatively few but very familiar words act as the operators. Words will change from one class to the other as time goes on, but while the child limits his utterances to two words, he will keep to this basic construction.

This is an extremely interesting stage in the child's language development because it is different from anything that has gone before. The sounds he makes and the words he uses are all copied from his mother but here suddenly is a development which we cannot think of as being copied from a pattern that is given to him. Mothers themselves are sometimes rather concerned and are often reproached by other people for 'teaching the child baby-talk'. The fact is that the boot is entirely on the other foot; it is the baby who teaches Mummy baby-talk. Adults do not spontaneously say things like 'all-gone milk', they only say them in imitation of the baby who is now creating his own language and not simply repeating what he hears. What is happening is very much a development in thinking as well as in language; the child is already grasping the principle that lies behind the use of verbs as well as nouns. From now on new words will be, not just new items all of one kind, but will fall into different classes because of the different ways in which they are used.

When two-word phrases are well-established it is not very long before the child extends his technique to strings of three or four words, still using only words that are essential to his meaning. Although many of his phrases now begin to sound like adult sentences, he will quite often use his own order for the words and say things like: "Mummy biscuits got" or "Where you are?", which show that he is still developing afresh the technique of making up sentences and not simply copying the strings of words he hears from adults. At the same time, patterns for adult sentence constructions are being given to him all the time and it is of course eventually by imitating these that he brings his own into line with what everyone else is doing, so that the continual feeding of speech to the child is just as vital as ever it was, especially if he is deaf.

The time the child takes to get from his first two-word phrases to sentences which are for the most part indistinguishable from those of an adult speaker is remarkably short and in the process he performs feats of deduction which, if one looks at them coolly, are really quite extraordinary. Just from hearing examples in the speech of adults around him he deduces for example that in English if you want to talk about something which happened in the past, you most often add -ed to one class of words, that if you have more than one of a particular thing you add -s to another class of words, that if some quality is more in one case than another you put -er on the end of the word that refers to it, and so on. In this way in a very short space of time his brain is stocked with the principal laws of English grammar, for they are laws which obtain and not rules that ought to be kept. You may feel impelled to say that surely these are things which we do not learn until we go to school, but nothing could be further from the truth. All that happens at school is that an attempt is made to bring into the light of day some part of the vast mass of information which we already have stored in our brain about our native language. Or you may wonder whether we can be sure that the young child does go through the process that has been described. One has only to listen to children's speech for a very short time to collect the evidence about this because once the child has deduced a certain law, like those mentioned above, he will apply it generally and make up expressions by analogy with those he has already noted. Having discovered how to make verbs refer to the past by adding -ed, he will use forms like *bringed* and *teached*. People are inclined to say that this is because he has not yet learned English grammar, but in fact he does it because he *has* learned English grammar, or rather has deduced the main laws for himself. In the natural course of events, as he hears more and more speech from others he will notice that in some cases other forms are commonly used as the past of the verb and quite soon he will be saying *brought* and *taught*. In a similar way he will use words like *sheeps* and *scissorses*, like *gooder* and *badder* until further listening experience leads him to replace them. All this forming of expressions by analogy is the essence of acquiring the grammar of his language. It can give rise to many interesting and charming examples like the case of the small boy who said: "You'd never do that, never'd you?" or of the father who called out to two sisters in another room: "Deborah, tell Elizabeth not to argue" and then heard a childish voice exclaim: "Elizabeth, don't arg me!"

The child's progress in building up the grammar of his language is all the time reflected in the rate at which different classes of words are built up. In the early stages, and certainly while utterances are confined to a single word, everything said is really the name of something and corresponds to adult nouns. When two words are put together, those we have called the operators are on the whole the forerunners of verbs but we cannot and should not equate the child's language with adult language; the function of the words may be different and sometimes more comprehensive. So in phrases like 'Mummy shoe', 'Mummy hat', 'Mummy coat' most frequently the child is simply referring to Mummy's shoe, etc., but on another occasion 'Mummy coat' may very well mean: 'Mummy must put her coat on so that she can take me out'.

In adult English the number of different words varies from one class of word to another. Nouns are the most numerous, with verbs next and adjectives some way behind. Adverbs are fewer still and then the other classes, prepositions, pronouns and conjunctions are relatively small. These proportions are reflected in a child's speech. He begins with a comparatively large stock of nouns and only one or two verbs, and then about the age of two he will generally increase his stock of verbs rather rapidly, though the number will never equal that of the nouns. At this stage he will have also a few adjectives, perhaps an adverb or so and one or two interrogative words like *what* and *where*. We have to realise that language development and mental development go hand in hand and interact very much with each other; the child's grasp of the relations of things in the outside world and his ability to perform particular mental operations do a great deal to determine the order in which some word classes grow. A child does not find it easy, for example, even to understand the meaning of prepositions and therefore does not use them in the early stages. When he is about two, he may acquire a few like *to*, *in*, and *on*, but it will be very much later before he can use words like *under*, *behind*, *before* and so on. In much the same way he may use the word *and* fairly early but he will not use *but* or *if* until he gets to the stage of forming complex sentences. It is quite understandable that one of the last word classes to be used is that of the pronouns because in simple sentences a noun can always be used instead. Up to the age of two or more a child generally refers to himself by name and in the third person and it is only after he starts referring to himself as *I* or *me* that other pronouns enter his vocabulary.

His capacity for constructing sentences must clearly depend on these various developments in his vocabulary. Like everything else in language it is essentially brain-work and it is brain-work which a child is perfectly capable of doing if only he is fed with enough speech, from his mother primarily and from everyone around him. Between the ages of six months and five years the ordinary child does an astonishing job in the field of language. He does it painlessly and we must remember that he is practising every waking moment. The only requirement is that he should be receiving sounds, the raw material for the job, all the time. If this condition is fulfilled, the child who has a hearing loss can make just as good a job of learning his mother tongue as a hearing child and if we can make it possible for him to do so, we shall have gone very far indeed towards over coming the disability with which he sets out in life.

An important aspect of the matter which this chapter has not dealt with is the specific effects that a hearing loss introduces into the situation. To understand these we have to know a good deal about the facts of physics, so the following chapter will give you first of all information about the acoustics of speech sounds and in the light of this will give an account of the effects that deafness introduces and show how far these may be overcome.

CHAPTER V

FACTS OF PHYSICS

What do we mean when we say that a child has a hearing loss, or is deaf? One thing that the statement does not generally mean is that there is no sound in the world loud enough for that child to hear. The expression 'hearing loss' itself is used to indicate simply that if we want him to hear a sound we have to give him a lot more sound energy than we would need to give to a normally hearing person. So the first physical fact that is important for us is that sounds do differ greatly in the amount of energy they contain. In one way or another we frequently have to deal with this aspect of sound in everyday life, although we may not be involved in any technical sense with such matters. To take a very straightforward example, if you were listening to the radio or the sound from a television set and a noisy aircraft began to circle persistently overhead, you would have to 'turn up' the sound, by using the volume control, in order to hear satisfactorily. What this does is to increase the amount of sound energy or intensity being sent out by the loudspeakers so that, as far as your ears are concerned, it exceeds the sound energy the aircraft is sending out.

We are all familiar enough with such ways of regulating sound energy in the case of sounds reproduced electronically. Most of the sounds we hear, however, even to-day, are reaching us in their natural form and we cannot so easily control their intensity. We do in fact have one means of doing so, but it is a rather inconvenient one. If we have to listen to a talk or lecture and we find that the speaker talks rather quietly, we can move to a seat much nearer to him; or if we are bothered by a noisy car or aircraft, we hope that it will move away from us. We can turn up the sound by getting nearer to it or turn it down by increasing our distance from it because sound energy or intensity falls off very rapidly as the distance from the source of the sound increases. In the noisy world of to-day this is on the whole very fortunate. The sound energy poured out by modern aircraft in and around a large airport, for example, is high enough to be a continual nuisance and people who happen to live in the neighbourhood are obliged to move a number of miles away if they want to reduce the sound to a bearable level. The majority of us are fortunate enough not to have to spend all our working hours within three feet of a pneumatic drill or inside a cotton mill or a boiler-maker's shop and if we come into contact with such things at all it is usually at a safe distance or for a short time. On the other hand, if you live in a large city it is quite possible that your surroundings are never quiet enough for you to hear leaves rustling or birds singing because the sound energy in these sounds is low compared with the continuous hum of city noise.

Much of what we need to know about speech and hearing is bound up with the matter of sound energy or intensity so that we obviously need some terms in which to talk about it, some scale on which we can compare sound intensities and some units in which to measure it. The unit which is used to express intensity is one that everyone is familiar with, the *watt*. We generally think of this only in connection with electricity but we know, for instance, that if we are working under a lamp and feel we need more light, we can get it by replacing a 60 watt lamp, say, by a 150 watt lamp. The intensity of the light is very much increased by doing this. When we turn up the volume of a radio set we are increasing the number of watts of sound energy being sent out by the loudspeaker.

The obvious thing, then, would seem to be to talk about sound intensity in terms of watts but in fact there are two considerable snags about doing this. The first stems from the fact that the general level of sound energies is very small indeed compared with the kinds of energy which are usually measured in watts. The ear itself is an incredibly sensitive receiver of sound, that is to say that it will detect, in suitable conditions, very low levels of sound energy indeed. If you were placed in a very efficient sound-proof room, from which all the sounds of ordinary life were drastically excluded, it would be possible to find out what was the very smallest sound intensity that your ear could perceive. If you have normal hearing this would be about 0.0000000000000001 watts. This is a very unwieldy kind of figure and we can promise for one thing not to print it again in this book, but it does show that talking about sound intensities in terms of watts is not altogether convenient. Even when we come to deal with much louder sounds, things are only marginally better. We may, for example, think that some of our acquaintances talk rather loudly but in fact we should need more than one million people all talking at once to produce the level of energy required to light an ordinary 60 watt light bulb.

The second difficulty is that in the world of sound we are most of the time interested in comparing sound intensities; how much more sound energy shall I collect if I move six feet nearer to the speaker; how much must I turn up the volume of my radio so that I can hear it comfortably above the aircraft noise, how far should I have to reduce the sound intensity coming through from my neighbour's flat in order not to go crazy every time his kids practise the piano? In these circumstances, if we were dealing in watts, we should have to compare two unwieldy numbers each time and be quite likely to come out with an unwieldy answer too. The unit which in practice is used to express sound intensities has been designed to take care of both difficulties at the same time and it is as a result a rather peculiar affair. The *decibel* or *db.* is nowadays an item in everyone's passive vocabulary and in most people's active vocabulary too. Modern noise problems are so acute that we have all been forced into some degree of familiarity with the units in which noises are measured and there is no reason why we should not talk about decibels as though they were exactly like pints of milk, pounds of tea or yards of rayon. However, if you have persevered with this chapter up to this point and, more seriously, if you are at all closely concerned with the problem of hearing and deafness, you will find it helpful to understand how the decibel differs from these more homely units of measurement and in particular how it gets over the difficulties that have been mentioned.

In order to get round the problem of long numbers all that is needed is a different way of writing them. There is nothing wrong with the numbers in themselves, they just call for a different notation. Newspapers to-day are continually having to refer to the astronomical, in more ways than one, sums of money extracted from the pockets of the suffering taxpayer and in doing so they print things like £12M or £200M rather than put in six noughts. This is simply an example of choosing a new way of writing numbers. In the case of the decibel, the method used is just a traditional mathematical one which consists in using the logarithm of a number instead of the number itself. Basically this is writing 100 as 10^2 and 1,000,000 as 10^6 and so on. Using this notation, the rather fearsome number that was printed above appears as 10^{-16} watts. You will no doubt realise that when you see numbers of decibels quoted they do not appear in this form, but this is because in the decibel system, the 10 itself is not printed.

The other feature of the decibel is that it always refers to the ratio between two sound intensities, it tells us that one intensity is so many times greater than another. It is rather as though you asked someone: "How long is your dining-table?" and he answered: "Well, you know the table in my study? It's two and a quarter times as long as that." This would not be very satisfactory for lengths but it does work out extremely well in practice for sound intensities. The unit originally adopted for the purpose was the *bel*, named in honour of Alexander Graham Bell, who was an engineering student at University College London in the 1860's and later invented the telephone. It was found that the bel was too large for most purposes and so it was replaced in practice by the decibel, one-tenth of a bel. In order to use the decibel we have of course to measure the two sound intensities we are interested in (in watts) and then find how many times the one is greater than the other. We then look up the logarithm of this number and multiply it by ten, so that the answer shall be in decibels and not bels. Suppose for example that you are talking in ordinary conversation to someone who is a few feet away from you and for some reason you drop your voice to a whisper. The sound intensity now reaching his ear is reduced by about 10,000 times (big numbers again!); the ratio of the intensity of the conversational voice to the whisper is 10,000:1; the logarithm of 10,000 is 4 (because it equals 10^4), we multiply this number by 10 to get decibels and this gives us 40 db. Therefore the difference in sound energy in the two cases is 40 db. To take another example, imagine that you are standing in a garden in a quiet suburban street when a pneumatic drill starts up about ten feet away from you. The sound energy reaching your ears would go up by 1,000,000 times; the logarithm of the ratio is 6 and the increase would therefore be 60 db. To take a much smaller ratio, doubling the intensity of a sound brings about an increase of 3 db., since the logarithm of 2 is 0.3, and ten times this value is 3. Notice that any doubling of the energy yields only a 3 db. increase; if you were exposed to the sound of an operatic soprano singing top C fortissimo at a distance of six feet and she were joined by another singing at the same volume, the resulting increase in sound intensity would be 3 db.; you could perhaps console yourself with the knowledge that it would take *two* more of equal calibre just to raise the sound level by a further 3 db.—but perhaps we had better leave the example there.

When decibel values are given in the press and elsewhere there is generally little mention of the comparison of sound intensities; it may be stated quite simply that, for example, the noise from a jet aircraft is 120 db., or something of this nature. What then has happened to the ratio of which the decibel value is an expression? Are two sounds being compared in this case and if so, what are they? The answer is that for many purposes sound energies are compared with that minute amount of energy mentioned above, 10^{-16} watts, as being somewhere about the threshold of human hearing. This has been adopted as a common reference level, so that when a decibel value is given and only one sound is referred to, it is implied that the given intensity is so many decibels above 10^{-16} watts. Aircraft noise of 120 db. therefore is 120 db. more intense than this reference level, which means by the way that it is one million, million times greater in energy. An advantage of adopting such a low level as our reference is that all sounds we are dealing with are going to be above it, but clearly this would be impractical were it not for the logarithmic character of the decibel which in this case reduces the 13-figure ratio to the number 120.

Anyone who comes in contact with the problem of deafness, whether in children or adults, is very soon introduced to the decibel because the commonest way of expressing hearing loss is in terms of these units. In this context, the reference level is the threshold intensity for the normally hearing population, that is to say the sound energy which is just perceptible by most people. When this value is measured, in watts, it is found that it varies according to the frequency of the sound being heard, that is it depends on whether the sound is high-, medium- or low-pitched. The ear is most sensitive to sounds in the middle of its range, round about 2000 cycles per second, much less sensitive to high frequency sounds and still less sensitive to very low frequencies. Measurements have been made for a very large number of individuals and from these has been determined the average intensity needed at many different frequencies to produce the sensation of hearing. As we said at the beginning of this chapter, when we say someone has a hearing loss we mean that it takes more sound energy, at particular frequencies, to produce the sensation of hearing for him than for a normally hearing person. This greater amount is compared with the normal average and the ratio is expressed in decibels, so that if someone were said to have a hearing loss of 60 db. at 4000 cycles per second, this means that at that frequency he needs one million times as much sound energy as the normal person to hear anything at all.

The Energy in Speech Sounds

It follows logically from what has been said, as well as being obvious from practical experience, that a hearing loss will affect the hearing of speech just as it does that of other sounds. It is not, however, a very simple matter to establish hearing loss for speech, basically because the intensity of speech sounds is a very variable quantity. Apart from the fact that their intensity, like that of all other sounds, decreases as you get further away from the source, the speaker in this case, there are very considerable differences from one speaker to another and in the same speaker from time to time. We have already seen that when we are talking we do our best to maintain a satisfactory ratio between the sound of our own voice and any noise that may be surrounding us and in order to do this we make changes in the volume at which we talk at very frequent intervals. It is not only a matter of noise, of course, but of circumstances generally; when we talk to someone we know to be deaf, we talk more loudly, and when we have anything very confidential to say we 'lower our voice'. The best we can do in this situation is to make a great many measurements of intensity and to take average values as being representative of speech in given conditions. First we must adopt some standard distance from the speaker, let us say 3 feet as being a reasonable conversational distance; then we settle some further conditions, speech in an ordinary conversational voice in a quiet room, and find the average of many intensity measurements made in these conditions. The result of these measurements is a figure of 60 db. Since no comparison is explicitly made here, this means of course 60 db. above the reference level of 10^{-16} watts. If we take the corresponding figure for speech when the speaker is talking as loudly as he can (still at a distance of 3 feet), the average rises to 75 db.; when he drops his voice to a very low level, but not actually whispering, the average is 40 db. and for a whisper, 20 db. In different conditions, then, the average intensity of speech can vary as much as 55 db.

The matter of the general intensity level of speech is extremely important when we are dealing with the deaf child. There are several reasons why it would be unpractical to expect a mother to talk continually at the top of her voice to her child, the most important of which is that she could not possibly keep it up and she would be exhausted in a very short time. But it is possible for her to reduce the distance between herself and the baby and many deaf children who now have excellent speech and are in normal schools owe all this to the fact that their mothers adopted the method of speaking very close to their ear when they were younger. By reducing the distance in this way, the intensity of even conversational voice is raised to about 85 db. and the level can be brought higher still by talking more loudly. Hearing aids are first and foremost devices for bringing up the intensity of sounds that fall upon them and they may do so by as much as 80 db. Their function is to make sounds audible, especially the sounds of speech, which would otherwise be inaudible and they therefore play a very important part in giving the deaf child the sound stimuli which we have seen are so vital for the development of speech and language.

Another kind of variation in intensity is always present in speech, in addition to that introduced by talking loudly or softly as occasion demands. This is due to the fact that in the sound system of any language there are some sounds which are naturally of rather high intensity and others which are naturally of lower intensity. In English this is a good deal bound up with the structure of the syllables that occur in words. We can notice differences in the number of syllables, for example, in *teapot*, which has two, *appetite*, which has three, *amplification*, which has five and *thought*, which has one. From a physical point of view, each time a syllable occurs there is a peak in the amount of sound energy so that the number of syllables corresponds to a number of bulges in intensity, as it were. If we measure intensity continuously when someone says *appetite* we shall record three of these bulges, five for *amplification* and only one for *thought*. A bulge implies that there is a lower level of intensity of either side and this is indeed the case; a syllable is made up of a vowel sound, which provides the high level of intensity, with a consonant on either side, which is of relatively low intensity. You will notice that this does not seem to be quite true for the first syllable in *appetite* or *amplification*, but if either of these words comes first in a sentence or is said by itself, then there is a silence before it, that is low or rather zero intensity, and if it occurs within a sentence, then the *a* is preceded by the final consonant of the previous word.

There are regular intensity differences then between the vowel or syllabic sounds and the consonant sounds in English, and there are further differences among the members of these two classes of sound. The range of these variations expressed in decibels is surprisingly wide. The faintest sound in the English sound system is *th*, as in *thought*, and the vowel sound with the greatest intensity is the vowel of this same word; the difference between them is nearly 30 db. Other vowel sounds are not quite so intense, but the weakest of them, the vowels in *tea* and *two*, are still about 20 db. more than *th*. The consonant sounds have intensities strung out over the rest of the range, with sounds like *l*, *m* and also *sh* from 15–20 db. above *th*, down to *p* and *f* which are only about 7 db. higher.

What this means in effect is that all the time you are listening to someone talking, your ear is receiving sounds of rapidly fluctuating intensity with the maximum differences covering a range of nearly 30 db. How is this variation related to the average figures given above for conversational, very loud and very soft speech? The value of 60 db. for conversational speech is simply the average of a great many intensity values which are scattered above and below 60 db. with a spread of approximately 30 db. in all. In speech the greater proportion of time is spent in the vowel and higher intensity sounds and a relatively small amount of time in the weakest sounds so that the peaks of energy will not be so very much in excess of 60 db. When the average changes, as it does in very loud or soft speech, the intensity differences between the various sounds are fairly well preserved; the succession of syllables is still easily perceived and the range of intensity remains in the region of 30 db. Even in whisper we have no difficulty in recognising the number of syllables that have occurred, but in this case the range of intensity is somewhat reduced because the sound of voice, which is what makes speech really audible, is no longer being used.

The rise and fall of intensity in speech has some important implications in the problem of the deaf child. It is quite possible for some parts of a speech sequence to be audible to a child with a hearing loss while other parts are not. These will be the high intensity or vowel parts, and it is by no means uncommon to come across a child who hears only the vowel parts of speech. In such a case the mother may perhaps say that she does not think her baby can be deaf because he turns when she calls his name. Unfortunately, however, if she calls out "Johnnie", for instance, the child will turn if he manages to hear just the high intensity vowel of the first syllable

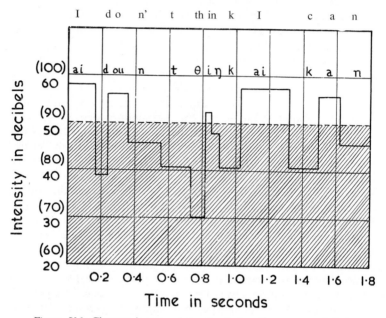

Figure V.1. Changes in mean intensity during the sentence *I don't think I can.* Only the sounds whose intensity is above the shaded area would be audible to a child with an overall hearing loss of 50 db. A hearing aid providing 40 db. of amplification would raise the intensity of the sounds to the values denoted by the figures in parentheses.

of the word. In this situation he has enough hearing to give a response but it is not enough to enable him to build up for himself the complex system of the English language. The kind of thing he will be hearing is shown in the hypothetical example of Figure V.1, which gives the intensity fluctuations in the sentence *I don't think I can,* using the average figures to represent the intensity of the succeeding sounds. Of course the intensity does not change in the step-like fashion shown here in real life, but the duration allotted to each sound is taken from an actual utterance of the sentence. The shaded area indicates how much of the sentence will lie below the child's threshold, given that he has a certain hearing loss. If you say the sentence over to yourself, keeping the natural rhythm but making only the vowels audible, you may begin to have some idea just how unintelligible such a version of speech would be and to appreciate the impossibility of learning the system on the basis of such information.

We saw earlier, when talking about the redundancy of the language that vowels carry rather less information than consonants; it turns out that unfortunately consonant sounds are less easily audible than vowels, and this presents a double handicap for the deaf child. The sounds which are most important for his understanding of other people's speech and for making his speech intelligible to others, are broadly speaking the sounds which are most likely to fall below his threshold of hearing. This is one more reason for ensuring that children have adequate and efficient hearing aids since through their use the intensity of sounds may often be raised to a level which is substantially above threshold. In Figure V.1 two sets of figures are given on the intensity scale; those in brackets indicate what the intensity of the various speech sounds would be if they could all be raised by 40 db. through the use of hearing aids. This is a hypothetical and indeed artificial example, but it shows the principle involved; all the sounds are brought well above the deaf person's threshold of hearing, indicated by the dotted line at 50 db. In this second condition, with the help of hearing aids, a child would have every chance of learning the language system and of speaking normally himself, but he would manage neither if left in the first condition in which he never hears anything but the peak of each syllable.

High and Low Frequencies in Speech

The intensity differences among speech sounds which have just been described are the result of the continuous movement of the tongue, lips, soft palate and other parts of the speech mechanism during speech. While consonant sounds are being articulated, the air passage from the throat out through the mouth is either partly or completely closed at some point, so that sound intensity is reduced, and during vowel sounds the passage is more widely open along its whole length, with a resulting increase in intensity. These movements have other and equally important effects on the sounds produced in speech, which are related to the various frequencies which make up the sounds. Any sound, whether speech or some other kind of sound, is made up of a mixture of frequencies. It may be composed predominantly of low frequencies, and will therefore sound low-pitched, it may have predominantly high frequencies and sound high-pitched, it may have its energy concentrated in the middle frequencies or spread over a wide range of frequencies. It is important for the understanding of our subject to have some clear idea of what such differences mean and we can probably gain this in part from simple examples. Try saying out loud the two English sounds, *s* and *sh*, by prolonging the last sounds in the words *puss* and *push*. Say each sound by itself and then alternate them, going back and forth from one to the other. Your ear will soon tell you that one difference between the two sounds is that of pitch: *s* has the higher pitch and *sh* the lower. If you are at all musical, you will probably succeed in whistling two notes which give roughly the difference in pitch between the two sounds. We perceive this difference because the sound energy in *s* is concentrated in the high frequency region, most of it above 4000 cycles per second (c.p.s.) while in *sh* the energy spreads further down the frequency scale to somewhere a little below 2000 c.p.s.

To take another example, prolong the sound in the middle of *hissing* and the one in the middle of *buzzing*; while these two sounds are going on, put your finger and thumb on your Adam's apple and you will notice that during *z* there is a continual vibration going on in the larynx which is not there while you say *s*. This vibration of the vocal cords, which lie within the larynx, adds some low frequency energy to the sound; apart from this the actual noises of *s* and *z* are very similar and both high-pitched, so that the latter has two main regions in which there is sound energy, the high one, from 4000 c.p.s. upwards and a low one, round about 100 or 200 c.p.s. The vocal cords are vibrating during the majority of English sounds and whenever they do so they contribute a certain amount of low frequency energy. For all the vowel sounds, the energy is mostly confined to this region and the middle frequency range, up to about 2000 c.p.s. You may find it useful to compare other sounds for yourself and to try to decide roughly where most of their energy lies; for example to see how *f* compares with *m*, or *t* with *b*, but in doing so you have to be careful to make sure that you are making the sound just by itself and not combining it with another sound, or of course saying the name of the letter.

The reason why this aspect of speech is so very important is that hearing loss or deafness also varies with the frequency of sounds; in other words no-one is equally deaf to all frequencies. In a later chapter an account is given of the various types of deafness. For the moment we shall take a very over-simplified view of their characteristics in order to get some idea of the interaction we have to expect between the deaf ear and acoustic features of speech.

Effects of Deafness on Speech Reception

It was said earlier that amount of hearing loss is specified by comparing the sound energy a normal ear requires in order to just hear a given frequency with that required by a deaf ear. The necessary

intensity measurements can be made with adults and with older
children and they are expressed in a standard form which is called
the pure-tone audiogram. This is simply a curve on which is plotted
for each frequency tested the number of decibels by which the
sound has to be increased so that the patient shall just hear it
(threshold intensity). Generally a separate curve is drawn for a
patient's right and left ear. Among people who have a hearing loss
there are differences in the audiogram from person to person and
usually between the two ears in the same person, but there are some
useful generalisations that can be made about types of hearing loss
and types of deafness.

One type of audiogram which frequently occurs shows a hearing
loss predominantly for low frequencies, below about 1000 c.p.s.,
with a smaller degree of loss for high frequencies, above about
3000 c.p.s. Such an audiogram is generally associated with a conductive deafness (see p. 85), that is to say an abormality affecting the
transmission of sound by the ear-drum and the middle ear. When
sounds are received by a conductively deaf ear any low frequency
energy they contain is considerably reduced or attenuated. The
low frequency components in speech are mainly responsible for
making the speech audible to the listener. When we whisper, for
example, we switch off completely the vocal cord mechanism in the
larynx and thus reduce very substantially the low frequency content
of the speech. Whisper is certainly much less audible than speech
that is normally voiced. Speech heard by someone with a conductive
deafness therefore appears to be very much softer than it does to
the ordinary person. Fortunately this lack of power can be very
successfully made good by the use of a hearing aid which can
amplify all the speech sounds so that they now appear much louder
to the listener.

A second type of audiogram is one which indicates a loss for high
frequencies rather than low, often from about 2000 c.p.s. upwards.
This denotes a perceptive or nerve deafness, an abnormality in the
inner ear or in the nerve connections to the brain. Naturally this
does mean that high frequency components are attenuated on
reception by the ear but it means much more than that. An ear
suffering from perceptive deafness introduces a distortion of the sound
which as far as we can judge must be something like the effect of
making a loudspeaker blast by overloading it with too much power;
this changes the nature of sounds and makes them difficult to recognise and to distinguish from each other. Along with this defect goes
another which is related to it, and this is that such ears are particularly
sensitive to loud sounds. While low intensity sounds are either
inaudible or very faint to the perceptively deaf ear, loud sounds
appear just as loud as they do to a normal ear or in some cases

even louder. This combined with the distortion just mentioned above makes listening very difficult for the person with perceptive deafness.

As far as speech is concerned, the perceptively deaf are far worse off than those with a conductive deafness. All the latter require is that the speech should be made loud enough and this can be done by a hearing aid, or indeed by talking close to the ear or shouting. The person with perceptive deafness is the one who, though deaf, continually says "Don't shout, I can hear you!". It is true that he can hear you but generally he finds it difficult to understand what is being said to him because of the distortion which his ear introduces. For the reception of speech he is in the worst possible position; first, he suffers attenuation of high frequencies, which are particularly important components of many consonants and, as we have seen, the consonants carry the larger part of the information in speech; second, the low intensity sounds, and again this means the consonant sounds, remain very faint or below threshold, while the high intensity sounds, the vowels, are louder than they would be for a normal ear; third, the quality of all the speech sounds is subject to some degree of distortion.

Can anything in the way of a hearing aid help someone who is in this very difficult situation? Modern aids can fortunately do a great deal for him, because they can be designed to bring all sounds with a certain restricted range of intensity; that is to say they may raise the energy level of weak sounds, like many of the consonants, and at the same time ensure that high intensity sounds are amplified very little or not at all, so that they never get so loud as to be painful or disturbing to the deaf person.

In addition to cases of conductive and perceptive deafness, it is not uncommon to find ears which suffer from both conditions at the same time. The audiograms for all three classes may well show hearing loss for both high and low frequencies or indeed over the whole frequency range. This is particularly the case in children born deaf or becoming deaf at an early age. In severe cases, in fact, it may turn out that the child has hearing for only a very small range of frequencies, perhaps from 200 to 1000 c.p.s. In such cases hearing aids are more than ever indispensable because they give the child a chance of continually using the restricted hearing which is left to him. The speech heard by those of us with normal hearing contains frequencies covering a range from approximately 100 to 8000 c.p.s. Is it possible then that a child with such a small range of usable hearing can learn to hear and to speak? Incredible as it may seem, it is possible and in the following section we shall try to show why and how it can be done, that is insofar as we are at present able to explain the process.

How the Deaf Hear

The first factor in the situation is the one referred to at the beginning of the previous chapter; as normally hearing people, we do not need anything like the amount of information that reaches us in speech in order to recognise and understand what has been said. Just as we can read a line of print that is only half there, so we can understand speech transmitted over a telephone line which is sending us only the frequencies from 300 to 3000 c.p.s. instead of the full range from 100 to 8000 c.p.s. We have to remember that we are doing this after having learned to read or understand speech, but still it is a good indication that much of the information we normally receive could be dispensed with.

An even more important fact, however, is that learning to recognise something is a matter of *organising* the information we receive, it is not implicit in the sensory impressions themselves. This is true of any kind of recognition. To take a rather crude example, distorting mirrors, such as were once fairly common in fun-fairs, give you an image of yourself which is immediately recognisable, despite the fact that if you made careful measurements on it you would not find any figure that corresponded with a measurement of your real self; the image may be highly entertaining or it may be absolutely awful, but you know that it is you. To take another example along the same lines, there is a small proportion of people in the world who are colour blind and yet who manage to move around and behave in almost every respect as do people who are without this peculiarity. They recognise and classify things just like everyone else and it is almost impossible to detect that someone of our acquaintance is colour blind unless he himself gives us the information in a very specific way. If an American visitor to London confides to you that he had some difficulty at first in recognising the 'mail-boxes because they were all green', you would realise that he does not see what you see. But the fact remains that he does recognise a pillar-box and has no difficulty in posting his letters. In a similar way, a colour blind person is no more likely than the rest of us to be killed at traffic lights; most of us look primarily at the colour of the light, but the colour blind person, even if he cannot distinguish between the colours, can rely with complete safety on the relative position of the lights. Again it is his organisation of the information that is important rather than the particular bits of information he has at his disposal.

We can have no doubt that the deaf child, when he hears speech, hears something different from what most of us hear. He is getting less information because of the reduction in the frequency and intensity range introduced by his hearing loss, and he may also be receiving sounds that are transformed by some other kind of distortion in his hearing mechanism. It is very hard for those of us who have normal hearing to understand how, in these circumstances, the child can ever learn to understand speech. Our basic difficulty is that we tend to believe subconsciously that the sounds of our language are fixed units which come up in the same form every time the 'same' thing is said. If we think about this matter for only a few minutes, however, we are bound to realise that this is not the case. Imagine just one single syllable, let us say the word 'no', said by a wide variety of speakers, the proverbial Englishman, Irishman and Scotsman plus a Welshman, an Australian, a New Zealander, a South African, a Canadian, an American, an Indian etc. Each one would make the sounds differently from all the others and what is more we should have no difficulty in hearing that they were different yet we should recognise the word 'no' in every case, because we should fit the sounds into the right place in the system. Once again it is a question of operating with the whole system rather than depending on the specimen of a sound which hits our ears at a given moment.

We have already used the parallel of handwriting in this connection. It is quite clear that if we got one hundred individuals to write a single letter of the alphabet, no two of the resulting shapes would be identical. If it were not so, handwriting experts would be out of business! And yet we manage to read handwriting (at any rate most people's most of the time). In order to do this we have to only be able to *distinguish* each of the 26 letters from the others (each of 52 if we include the capitals). We can even tolerate some confusion among the letters, since we can rely upon the redundancy of the language to settle difficult cases. This distinguishing or discriminating things from one another is done by the use of what we may call *cues* for recognition, that is to say particular items of information which we form a habit of taking special notice of. All our recognition of things involves cues of one kind or another; we may perhaps catch sight of a friend or relation in the street and he may be walking away from us wearing a brand new suit but we say: "I recognised him from his walk." From long habit our brain has available many items of information about this person, about the way he raises his feet and puts them down, the pace at which he does it, the way he stumps, rolls or minces along; these are cues which enable us to say with absolute certainty "That is so-and-so!". Notice, by the way, that we could almost certainly do this particular feat of recognition if we could see nothing of the person above the waist; that is to say there is a lot of visual information about him that we can dispense with for this purpose.

The task of discrimination and recognition is one for which the human brain is superbly designed. It learns very readily what needs to be noticed in a given situation, what cues it must latch on to, and furthermore it is extremely flexible in this respect so that if conditions make a particular cue useless, it will use an alternative cue. Without this valuable capacity we should be incapable of reading handwriting, at least anything other than copper-plate. As it is, we need only a few seconds of practice to deal successfully with handwriting in which, say, a *t* is never crossed or an *i* dotted, and learn to discriminate the two letters perhaps by the height to which they ascend.

The reception of speech is the field in which this capacity of the brain is most fully exploited. During the period when we are learning to talk, our brains are busily collecting cues, that is items of information about speech sounds, which enable them ever afterwards to distinguish each one of the forty sound units from all the others in a great variety of contexts and conditions. The only requirement is that these cues should work. We do know something about the kinds of cue that normally hearing English speakers use and, as we should expect, there is some degree of common practice among them. This is not particularly important, however, for an individual is quite free to use any cues he likes, provided they work, that is to say provided he does not constantly make mistakes, in much the same way as the colour blind person is perfectly at liberty to read traffic lights by their position instead of their colour, provided he does not make mistakes (which might have rather serious consequences in this case).

There can be no doubt that this notion of cues for recognition is not a particularly easy one to grasp when one first encounters it, so it may be as well to give an example from English to illustrate the point. We will take four English words which rhyme, at least for many speakers in the south of England: *fought, thought, sought* and *short*. The words are distinguished by the first sound in each case, *f*, *th*, *s* and *sh*. Of course when any of these words occurs in running speech, we do not usually have to decide which of the four sounds has occurred because the context will make it almost certain which word it is. However we are capable of distinguishing these sounds from each other, and if someone just pronounced one of the words by itself at random, we should know which it was. The example of *s* and *sh* was given earlier on and we saw that most of the sound energy in *s* is from 4000 c.p.s. upwards, while that in *sh* is from about 1800 c.p.s. upwards. In *f* and *th*, the peak of the sound energy is higher still than for *s*, mostly between 6000 and 8000 c.p.s. So here is one cue, a frequency cue, which can be used in distinguishing these four sounds from each other: if the noise we hear is relatively low pitched, the sound must be *sh*; if it is somewhat above this, it is *s* and if it is very high pitched, it is—

either *f* or *th*. The frequency cue will not do the whole job since it leaves these two sounds undifferentiated. Another cue is needed here and this is provided by the fact that the vowel sound starts up in a slightly different way after each of the sounds *f* and *th*. We have no idea that we can detect such differences, but we do in fact do so. There is yet a further cue that can be used in recognising these four sounds, and that is the fact that the total sound energy is different; both *s* and *sh* are high intensity sounds while *f* and *th* are very low intensity sounds. These three cues can be used in a variety of ways and of combinations, according to circumstances. We could imagine a logical, computer-like routine which would go like this:

    i. Is the sound high or low intensity?
    ii. If high, is it high or low frequency?
    iii. If low intensity, is the vowel *f*- or *th*-type?

A good number of experiments have been done with speech sounds to try and discover some of the ways in which the brain uses cues of this kind. One reason for choosing the four sounds *f*, *th*, *s* and *sh* as our example is that there is also some information on how far deaf subjects are able to discriminate among these sounds. A group of deaf people which included some with hearing losses of 70 db. at 200 c.p.s. and 100 db. at 4000 c.p.s. were tested with random arrangements of syllables beginning with these sounds. Such hearing losses ought logically to dispose completely of the frequency cue and go far towards obliterating the intensity cue, leaving only cues depending mainly on the vowel sound. The actual results of the tests were that the deaf people recognised *sh* correctly 87 per cent of the time, *s* 83 per cent, *f* 77 per cent and *th* 72 per cent. What is the explanation of this? It is that hissing noises, like these four speech sounds, have sound energy spread very widely over the whole range of frequencies, so that there will be some even in the range below 2000 c.p.s. The deaf subjects, although deprived in a large measure of all the cues a hearing person would probably use, are able to develop their own cues out of the acoustic information they do receive. Once again, any cues can be used so long as they work.

This then is the essence of the task that faces the baby when he is acquiring the phonemic system of the language. It is external circumstances that tell him what things have to be distinguished from each other, that 'milk' is not 'cake', that 'cake' is not 'dolly' and so on, and his brain is set the task of finding cues that will allow him to get the right answer every time. If he has normal hearing, rather naturally he is likely to evolve the same cues as many other people have done. If he is deaf, he can still develop his system of cues but they will be specified in accordance with the acoustic information that he is deriving through his particular hearing apparatus. He is in the position of having to forge his own tools for the job, but the brain is quite equal to this and there is no reason why the tools should not be pretty well as efficient as those which the rest of us use.

How the Deaf Speak

We have now to deal with one final question and it is one to which the answer will inevitably appear rather complicated and hard to follow. For anyone who is directly concerned with the care and training of deaf children, however, the answer is of the greatest importance because it both offers an explanation of the many successes gained in the past and holds out real hope for all deaf children in the future.

It has been constantly maintained in this book, and it is an observed fact, that children born with a severe hearing loss cannot only learn to hear and to understand speech but can develop their own speech so that in many cases an ordinary listener cannot detect anything abnormal about it. The previous section showed how it is possible for the deaf child to achieve very satisfactory reception of speech by developing his own system of cues based on whatever acoustic information his ears provide him with. Earlier on we saw that the production of speech is very intimately bound up with hearing and that if a child is deprived of the sound of speech he will not succeed in learning the movements of speech for himself. But if this is true, how can a child with severely defective hearing himself produce speech which sounds like normal speech? If he can, then he must be sending out a great deal of sound energy which he himself cannot hear.

The answer is that he does indeed do this, and the explanation lies in the fact that the principle of using alternative cues works in the production of speech as well as in its reception. Let us revert to the example of sounds *s* and *sh* and try to follow closely the process by which a very deaf child could *produce* the difference between the two sounds. Imagine that he is able to detect practically no sound above 2000 c.p.s. He continually hears examples of the two sounds from his mother in circumstances which tell him that there is a necessary distinction to be made and eventually he can hear the difference between them by relying on the difference in energy *below* 2000 c.p.s. which is characteristic of *s* and *sh*. Now he tries to make the difference himself and in order to do so, he has to produce two sounds which, *for his own ear*, are differentiated by the same difference in energy below 2000 c.p.s. The only way in which he can successfully do this is by making movements, in this case mainly of the tongue and lips, which are very much like those which his mother herself makes, in other words he will be producing a fairly normal *s* and *sh*. He will of course be sending out a good deal

4

of sound energy above 2000 c.p.s. and indeed up to 4000 or 5000 c.p.s. and he will hear very little of this; if you like one can consider this as a kind of by-product of his attempt to match the pattern that he hears. The fact remains that by matching it, by reproducing the same difference in energy below 2000 c.p.s., he is sending out sounds which are very like the ones made by normally hearing people.

This is by far the major factor in the achievement of normal speech by severely deaf children. There are other more obvious ones, such as the fact that in some sound distinctions the child is materially helped by differences which he can and does see. When he adds the two sounds *f* and *th* to *s* and *sh*, for instance, he can see clearly differences in the action of lips and teeth and this helps him tremendously. Also he does have available, because they are within his range of hearing, the many cues supplied by the joining of consonant sounds to vowels, the distinction in this case between an *f*-vowel and a *th*-vowel. Valuable as these other aids are, however, they would not be sufficient in themselves to produce normal speech without the almost miraculous capacity of the brain for seizing on items of information of every kind and turning them to good use in achieving the desired end.

Those of us who have been much concerned to see that if possible every young deaf child should have the opportunity to take its place in the normal world, through its mastery of hearing and speech, could recount many incidents which reveal on the one hand the soundness of the view that deaf children can 'learn to hear', and on the other the persistent prejudice which leads many people still to advance one reason after another why the task is impossible. Some times the observation of the smallest detail may stick in one's mind and act ever afterwards as a powerful and convincing argument. This was so in the case of a small girl who was born with a hearing loss nowhere less than 90 db. in either ear. Though she lived in England, her mother was American and one day when she was making a recording she happened to tell us that she was taught by a private tutor, but she pronounced the word unmistakably to a British ear as 'tudor', in the American fashion. If ears with that degree of deafness can pick up such things from a mother's speech, what can they not do?

In the face of this kind of evidence it is sad that one should still encounter all too often the belief that deaf children ought to remain deaf, and even preferably dumb! One should hasten to add that the prejudice is certainly not to be found among the parents of the deaf children, but it does crop up among people who are professionally engaged in dealing with the deaf. When it does, the main objective often seems to be to prove that what has happened did not really happen; one may play recorded speech from a deaf child which is indistinguishable from that of a hearing child and show that the child's audiogram indicates a very severe loss in both ears. Sometimes the first line of 'defence' is the comment that surely this child was not born deaf. You may reply that indeed he was and this will bring forth further arguments, that the audiogram perhaps was not made at the time of the recording or the audiometer not properly calibrated and so on, often arriving at the final and, as it is thought to be, clinching argument with the comment: "Ah, but this is obviously a very intelligent child!". At this point we can leave the prejudiced observer since he has now underlined the main thesis of this book, that 'learning to hear' and 'learning to speak' are the work of the brain.

In this as in practically everything else the most intelligent child is apt to do best but the child of ordinary intelligence will do extremely well, provided he is given the help he needs. No one pretends that to do so is not an uphill task; it is, and most of all for the mother of the deaf child. But mothers are so often the last to complain, and any mother who has a deaf child has so much to gain if the task is successfully completed. All that is said about hearing and speech in these pages has only one end in view and that is to make the task if possible a little lighter and success more assured.

CHAPTER VI

TYPES AND CAUSES OF DEAFNESS

The emphasis so far in this book has been on hearing, although we have taken an occasional look at deafness. In this chapter we concentrate on deafness, its types and some of its causes.

TYPES OF DEAFNESS

Deafness may be classified from more than one point of view. One classification is **chronological.** *Congenital* deafness is present at birth; *acquired* deafness commences at some later date, either in childhood or in adult life.

Acquired deafness

In a child who has not yet learnt to speak acquired deafness has many of the characteristics of congenital deafness, although the child can still benefit, if properly helped, from the months of normal listening before he became deaf. Even older children who have learnt to speak will suffer more than adults because their speech habits are not yet fully established.

The age at onset of the deafness is of vital importance. In the first three years of life deafness results in an immediate arrest of all speech development and a rapid loss of the speech that has been learnt. At four or five years a child may lose his speech as quickly as six weeks after the onset of deafness. This interval lengthens with increasing age until at twelve years it may be a year.

The speed of onset of deafness also alters the effects on the child. *When deafness comes on gradually* there is time for some compensation to develop for the disability. For example, many children with a slowly developing deafness spontaneously achieve some proficiency in lip-reading. This spontaneous compensation is not, however, enough to overcome the disability and it is important that the deafness should be detected as early as possible in order that extra help may be given. This is the type of deafness which should be picked up on screening tests at school, but it can be detected more quickly if parents and teachers are aware of the possibility of deafness as a cause for deterioration in school work. In many cases the deafness is due to infection or catarrhal changes and can be improved or even cured by appropriate medical and surgical treatment. When this is not possible help must be given by getting a

84

good hearing aid, providing auditory training and arranging for the child to have a favourable position in class. Deafness due to catarrhal causes is often variable and requires careful follow-up. Deafness may occur for two to three months, during which the child misses so much at school that he is unable to catch up. A hearing aid may be necessary during these periods of deafness.

When the onset of deafness is sudden, as in the deafness due to meningitis, there is no time for compensation. The child is suddenly able to hear nothing but a few distorted sounds, which are quite insufficient for him to recognise speech. "I can hear your voice but cannot understand what you say," is the typical remark. It is important that the deafness should be detected quickly and auditory training started with a hearing aid (see page 98).

It must not be forgotten that sudden loss of hearing causes severe shock in addition to the shock of the illness which has caused it. Even the infant, deprived of the sounds he has heard, will inhibit response to any faint sounds which may still get through his diseased peripheral hearing mechanism. A condition analogous to separation and deprivation occurs and the child may appear far deafer than he really is.

Another classification of deafness depends on **the site of the lesion**. Deafness may be due to disease in any part of the hearing apparatus from the outer ear to the brain. Disease in the outer or middle ear interferes with the passage of sound waves to the inner ear. Disease in the cochlea interferes with the transformation of the sound waves into nerve impulses and disease in the acoustic nerve and in the nuclei and nerve tracts interferes with the passage of the nerve impulses to the cerebral cortex. Deafness due to disease of any of these organs is called *peripheral deafness* and is by far the most common. It may be conductive, perceptive or mixed. *Central deafness* is due to disease in the cerebral cortex, interfering with the interpretation of sound.

Conductive deafness

Disease in the outer or middle ear causes a conductive deafness. In pure conductive deafness the inner ear and the acoustic nerve are normal but cannot function normally because the sound waves reach them only in an attenuated or weakened form. The adult hearer is conscious that the sounds are fainter than normal, perhaps too faint to be understood at all. The deaf-born child will not hear sounds loud enough to learn that sound has any meaning.

Figure VI.1, showing the auditory sensation area, is of help in understanding the differing effects of conductive and of perceptive deafness. Sound frequencies (perceived as pitch) are measured along the horizontal lines of the graph, sound intensities (perceived as loudness) along the vertical lines. The auditory sensation area is bounded by two curved lines or *thresholds*. The lower is the *threshold of audibility*; below this level sounds are not audible. The upper curve is the *threshold of feeling*; above this level the sensation experienced is not one of sound but of feeling—at the threshold a sort of tickling sensation but as the intensity increases a sensation first of discomfort and then of pain.

Conductive deafness raises the level of both these thresholds, so that the extent of the auditory sensation area remains the same.

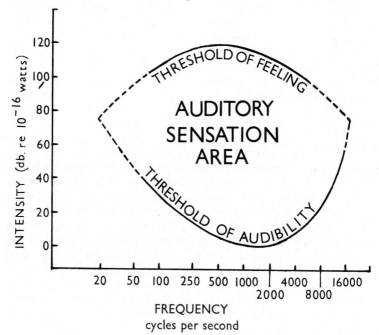

Figure VI.1. Auditory Sensation Area.
After 'Speech and Hearing', Harvey Fletcher, Macmillan, London.

The hearing loss is usually fairly uniform, although in some cases the loss may be mainly for high or low frequencies of sounds.

It follows from all this that it is relatively easy to assist the adult suffering from conductive deafness. Amplification of the sounds with a hearing aid overcomes the attenuation caused by the inter-ference with conduction of sound. Because the threshold of feeling is raised as well as the threshold of hearing it is possible to make speech audible without going above the threshold of feeling and causing discomfort. Because the hearing loss is more or less uniform the sounds amplified by the hearing aid will bear a close relationship to the sounds heard before the adult went deaf. There will be very little distortion of speech and very little auditory training or rehabilitation will be needed.

In the child who has not learnt the meaning of sound the situation is not so easy. He will not understand what is said to him the moment he is fitted with a hearing aid. All the aid can do is to enable sound to get through to the inner ear and on to the brain but the child must then have a long period of listening and learning to hear before he acquires comprehension hearing and can understand and produce speech.

Perceptive deafness

Another name for this is sensori-neural deafness because it is due to disease either in the sense-organ, the organ of Corti in the cochlea, or in the nerve pathway from the cochlea to the cortex—the acoustic nerve, the nuclei in the brainstem or the acoustic tracts.

High tones are usually affected before low tones. This has a considerable effect on the understanding of speech if the deafness comes on after speech has been learnt. Consonants are largely high-pitched sounds and so discrimination between consonants is difficult or impossible. Speech is distorted and recognition of distorted words must be learnt all over again. For the child born deaf distortion obviously does not arise because he has never heard words in the form that we regard as undistorted. Because of the increased facility to learn possessed by the very young child he can learn to make discriminations that are impossible to the adult. A visitor to the Nuffield Centre heard a recording of the speech of a deaf child, who enunciated clearly 'bru*sh*' and then '*church*'. "How can he possibly discriminate between 'sh' and 'ch'?" he asked for he had seen the child's audiogram (Figure IX.4, page 135) and knew that hearing was defective for the frequencies that are regarded as necessary to discriminate between these sounds. The answer must lie in the increased facility of the young child to learn and in his utilisation of alternative cues which are not used by the person with normal hearing because he can make the discrimination without their help.

A predominant loss of hearing for high tones means that hearing is relatively good for low tones. This brings a problem. Background noise consists mainly of low tones. It is therefore relatively well heard and masks what is left of hearing for high frequencies.

There is an intolerance to loud sounds in perceptive deafness, which affects the auditory sensation area in a very different way from conductive deafness. The threshold of audibility is raised but the threshold of feeling remains unaltered. As a result the extent of the auditory sensation area is greatly reduced. The intensity of a sound at the threshold of feeling will appear as loud to a person with perceptive deafness as to someone with normal hearing. This leaves very little room for manoeuvre; there is only a small interval between the intensity of sound that is just audible and the intensity that causes discomfort.

In many cases of perceptive deafness it is found that when the intensity of sound stimulation is increased step by step there is a far more rapid increase in the subjective sensation of loudness than in the normal subject. This phenomenon, which is not present in pure conductive deafness, is called *recruitment*. Intolerance of sound may occur even when the phenomenon of recruitment cannot be demonstrated. When recruitment is present patients will certainly be intolerant of sound.

Mixed deafness

This combines the characteristics of conductive and perceptive deafness. It is usually due to a conductive deafness with additional perceptive changes and occurs mostly in acquired deafness. It can also occur in congenital deafness when there is deformity of both the inner and the outer or middle ear.

Central deafness

This describes an inability to understand sound although the ear and the rest of the peripheral hearing apparatus are normal or nearly so. It must be due to disease in the cerebral cortex; as hearing is represented in both cerebral hemispheres the disease must be bilateral. This is extremely rare in an otherwise normal child, but one case was seen by EW. The cause was an accident at the age of 3 years. A special X-ray of the brain showed thinning of the cortex on both sides. The child had a normal pure tone audiogram but could not comprehend speech.

Usually central deafness is associated with some generalised disorder of the central nervous system, such as mental backwardness, psychosis or petit mal.

Central deafness in the deaf born child

A special form of central deafness is seen in the child who is born deaf or becomes deaf before he has acquired speech. The lesion here is not anatomical but physiological. Such a child has not had the chance to learn to hear. The cerebral cortex has not received sufficient sound stimulation for the meaning of sounds to be learnt and for comprehension hearing to develop. The presence or not of this central element in deafness is the main practical distinction between the deaf born child and the child or adult who becomes deaf after the acquisition of speech. Adequate auditory training enables the deaf born child to overcome this central element of deafness and leaves him with a much lesser disability comparable to that of acquired deafness. It is important to remember that there is a very real sense in which the child with normal hearing may be said to be born with 'central deafness'. The normally hearing child will lose this central deafness 'spontaneously'; the deaf child will require special help.

CAUSES OF DEAFNESS IN CHILDREN

Considerable advances have been made in the last three decades in our understanding of the factors that may result in the birth of a deaf baby. In spite of this it is still impossible to determine the cause in a very high proportion of cases. The following figures illustrate this. They are drawn from analyses published by various workers and cover cases going back nearly to the beginning of the century:—

1. In 1934 Yearsley published an analysis of 4,000 cases seen during 25 years. 1,284 were considered to be congenital. Of these 1,027 (80 per cent) were what is called 'sporadic' i.e. appearing without any known cause. The figures for acquired deafness show a completely different picture: out of a total of 2,935 only 105 ($3\frac{1}{2}$ per cent) are listed as 'doubtful'.
2. The next set of figures comes from Bordley and Hardy in 1952 after the great discoveries of rubella (German measles) and Rhesus incompatibility as causes of congenital deafness. Even so, 104 out of 296 are described as 'undetermined'. These are not subdivided into congenital and acquired but one can be sure from other series that most of the undetermined are congenital.
3. Whetnall in 1953 in an analysis of 800 cases gave 153 out of 491 congenital cases as 'sporadic'. This is a great improvement on the 1934 figure but the cause is still unknown for 31 per cent— nearly one in three.
4. Whetnall and Fry's analysis of a larger group in 1964 showed a higher percentage with cause unknown, 45 per cent or 502 from a total of 1,103 cases of congenital deafness. It is of interest that the total number of 3,047 children in this analysis included 1,157 who were not deaf—an encouraging indication of increasing awareness of the possibility of deafness and the need to refer doubtful cases for expert evaluation.

Continued research into the causation of deafness is important for several reasons. Increased knowledge may enable us to prevent deafness due to some causes, such as heredity, rubella and Rhesus incompatibility. With other causes, especially of acquired deafness, early recognition and treatment may reverse the disease process or reduce the disability. There is also the reason that it is psychologically more satisfactory for the parents to know the cause. Parents of handicapped children often bear an unnecessary load of guilt, feeling that in some way it is their fault that their child is handicapped. Knowledge of the cause of the disability helps them to take a more objective view of the matter and also helps them to decide whether it would be an unwarranted risk to have more children.

CLASSIFICATION OF CAUSES OF DEAFNESS

These causes are usually grouped nowadays according to the time when the disease process or disturbance of development takes place:—

I. *Pre-natal*, which includes inherited deafness and deafness due to some harmful factor during pregnancy;

II. *Peri-natal*, occurring at the time of birth;

III. *Post-natal*, occurring at any time after birth.

I. PRE-NATAL CAUSES

Hereditary

When Yearsley published his analysis in 1934 the only known pre-natal cause was heredity. In Whetnall and Fry's analysis (1964) over half the pre-natal cases were considered to be hereditary or familial. The term 'familial' is used when there is more than one case in a family but it is not clear that the condition is inherited. Only 32 of 191 cases fell into this group. Where the mode of inheritance has been worked out it may be either dominant or recessive. In dominant inheritance only one of the parents needs to have the relevant genetic factor. In recessive inheritance the child is not deaf unless both father and mother contribute the genetic factor. The study of genetics is becoming more exact and where there is any doubt parents should have the advantage of advice from a genetic expert. It seems reasonable that individuals with a dominant hereditary deafness should not have children; in recessive deafness the genetic constitution of both parents must be considered before a decision is taken.

The deaf educated in special schools by methods which do not fit them to mix in normal hearing society are very likely to spend the bulk of their social life in the company of the deaf, and to marry deaf partners. This increases the chance that their children will be deaf. Many deaf people do not realise the risks of marriage with another deaf person. They seek medical advice only after one, or even two, deaf children have been born. They should be better informed but best of all is to integrate the deaf as far as possible in normal hearing society. This will reduce the chance of intermarriage and is an additional advantage of early auditory training of deaf children and of the auditory approach in all their training and management.

Hereditary deafness may be a solitary defect or it may be associated with other defects. Certain groups of defects have been recognised and described as *syndromes of hereditary deafness*. One example is the Waardenburg syndrome. Some of the features of this syndrome are perceptive deafness, shortening of the eye fissures, irregular colouring of the iris, and overgrowth of the eyebrows. Not all members of a family exhibit all the features of these hereditary syndromes.

Non-hereditary

Maternal Rubella

Knowledge of the non-hereditary causes of deafness began with the observation in Australia of the association of congenital cataract with a history that the mothers had suffered from *rubella* (German measles) in early pregnancy. This was published in 1941 by N. McA. Gregg. Two years later C. Swan and other observers reported a series of similar cases and commented on the occurrence of other congenital defects—mainly perceptive deafness and cardiac defects. The later discovery of the cases of deafness illustrates the tendency for congenital deafness to be diagnosed late.

This discovery was the first evidence that it was possible for an infection in a pregnant woman to affect the developing foetus. Rubella remains the most frequent infection but cases are occasionally seen where no other cause for deafness can be discovered but the mother has suffered during early pregnancy from some other virus infection.

Not all epidemics of rubella are equally potent in causing defects in the foetus. There is no doubt that the epidemic in 1940 in New South Wales, Australia was the most severe so far recorded. It was concluded that infection in the first two months of pregnancy carried almost 100 per cent chance of a defective child in that epidemic. No doubt this high incidence contributed to the discovery of the connection. Although epidemics vary considerably in virulence there is always a cubstantial risk of congenital defect. A recent leading article in the *British Medical Journal* estimated that the risk might be about 25 per cent of some congenital defect in children whose mothers had rubella in the first sixteen weeks of pregnancy. Not all will include deafness among their defects, but the importance of maternal rubella as a cause of deafness is shown in the analysis in 1964 by Whetnall and Fry. In a total of 1,103 cases of congenital deafness 90 (just over 8 per cent) were due to maternal rubella, the largest group of known causes after heredity and Rhesus incompatibility.

The stage of pregnancy at which the mother has rubella is of great importance. The most dangerous time is in the first three months of pregnancy. This correlates with the extensive changes which are going on at this time in the developing foetus. The cochlea, for example, appears first as a curve in the fifth week of foetal life. By the third month all the coils of the cochlea are completed although the organ of Corti is not fully developed until later. Deafness appears predominantly when the infection occurs between the sixth and twelfth weeks of pregnancy, but a case has been seen in which the infection occurred before the mother knew she was pregnant. The rubella virus has been shown to persist for a long time and this presumably explains such a case.

It seems natural to expect that the disease process is quite different in hereditary deafness and deafness due to maternal infection. The opposite is true. The microscopic appearances in the cochlea of a child deaf from maternal rubella are indistinguishable from those present in some forms of hereditary deafness. One patient has even been seen where the full clinical picture of a syndrome of hereditary deafness was present and the mother had had rubella in the second month of pregnancy.

As the damage is in the cochlea the deafness is perceptive. It may affect one or both ears and may be moderate or severe. No case has been seen with bilateral total deafness. Recruitment (page 88) is frequently present. In one series of 34 EW found 20 (59 per cent) with recruitment. Intolerance of sound occurs even more frequently and the child deaf from maternal rubella should always have an aid with automatic volume control (see page 126).

General defects of development and behaviour are often present. The birth weight tends to be low, feeding difficulties are common, there may be delays in the appearance of the first teeth and in walking. Behaviour problems may cause great difficulty and concern to the parents. In many cases this appears to be connected with intolerance to sound and is aggravated by the use of an unsuitable hearing aid. A change to a more suitable aid with automatic volume control produces a wonderful improvement in personality, hearing and progress.

Prevention
Since the recognition of maternal rubella as a cause of congenital defects an enormous amount of research has been done on this infectious fever which had previously been considered a disease of little importance. Much thought has been given to the best way of preventing infection of pregnant women. Obviously it is important that the public should know the risk and that women who are pregnant, or who might be pregnant, should avoid exposure to the infection. In spite of all precautions some pregnant women will still suffer exposure to the infection. Attempts have therefore been made to spread immunity to the disease. The virus that causes rubella was isolated in 1962 and more recent research has produced several vaccines. The next problem is how best to use the vaccines. There has already been an International Conference on Rubella Immunisation. The ideal is total eradication of the disease as has almost completely happened in this country following mass vaccinations against smallpox and diphtheria. We do not, however, know how long immunity will last and vaccination in childhood might be followed by a breakdown in immunity just when the child-bearing age is reached. Vaccination of fertile women runs the risk of actually infecting a foetus with the vaccine. Tests have been developed to distinguish those who have immunity from those who are still susceptible. One suggested programme is to start by vaccinating all susceptible women in the period immediately after childbirth when it can be certain that they are not pregnant and there is less likelihood that they will soon become pregnant. Vaccination could next be extended to girls just below the age of puberty and finally to all children. In the meantime, if a woman develops rubella during early pregnancy the most reasonable course seems to be termination of the pregnancy by a therapeutic abortion.

Drugs
Various drugs have been reported as causes of congenital deafness. The one that has achieved the most publicity is thalidomide. The effects of this drug taken in pregnancy have led to a very careful scrutiny of new drugs from the point of view of possible ill-effects on the foetus. As is well known the principal deformities caused by thalidomide are in the limbs but the auricles may be deformed or absent and there may be atresia of the external auditory meatus (absence of the earhole).

Deformities of the outer and middle ear
This seems an appropriate place for a few remarks on deformities

of the outer and middle ear in general. Deafness due to pre-natal causes is nearly always perceptive but deformities of the outer and middle ear do occur. Congenital deformities of the outer and middle ear seldom occur together with defects in development in the inner ear. This is not surprising because the evolutionary and embryological development of the inner ear is distinct from the development of the other parts. Defects in development do sometimes occur together in all parts but from the practical point of view it is reassuring to know that the chances of a satisfactorily functioning inner ear are good in cases of deformity of the outer and middle ear. This means that in the majority of cases the deafness is conductive and should be remediable by surgical measures to overcome the mechanical impediment to the passage of the sound waves to the oval window of the inner ear. In atresia of the meatus a plastic operation is done to form an artificial ear hole. In middle ear deformity the operative procedure depends on the exact defect present; sometimes the procedure used is similar to one of the operations for the relief of otosclerosis in adult life. These operations for outer and middle ear deformity should take place as early as is feasible so that the child may benefit from the early years of facility in learning to hear. The alternative to operation is a bone conduction hearing aid which is difficult to keep in place. Even when plastic operations on the external auditory meatus fail to improve hearing, the new ear hole does at least allow the fitting of the more efficient insert type of hearing aid.

Sometimes the deformity affects only the auricle and the external auditory meatus is normal. We have seen that the human auricle has very little function, and absence of the auricle has only a slight effect on hearing. Plastic surgery may be necessary for cosmetic and psychological reasons.

Much of the surgery we have been describing calls for co-operation between a plastic surgeon and an otologist or ear surgeon. The early deaths of E. W. Peet and Gavin Livingstone dissolved a happy combination which had developed at Oxford.

II. PERI-NATAL CAUSES

Kernicterus

Not long after the discovery that maternal rubella could cause deafness, there was another discovery that explained a further large group of cases of congenital deafness. In 1944 Coquet reported the presence of deafness in kernicterus and since then many cases have been seen. This condition accounted for 148 (over 13 per cent) of the cases of congenital deafness in Whetnall and Fry's 1964 analysis—the largest group except for heredity.

Kernicterus is part of a general disease of the new born which results in a spastic child even more often than a deaf child. The general condition is known as haemolytic disease of the new born or erythroblastosis foetalis. Much study has been devoted to its elucidation in recent years and more can now be done to prevent and treat it. The red cells of the blood have a shortened life span because of an action allied to the immune reactions involved in resistance to infection. These immune reactions result in the production of specific *antibodies* which combat the infecting organism and cause its destruction. In haemolytic disease of the newborn the reaction occurs in the mother and is not related to an outside infection but to some incompatibility in the red cells. The resulting antibodies are called specific *iso-antibodies* (Greek *isos* = same). They occur most often because of a factor in the red cells called the Rhesus or Rh factor, first discovered in work with the red cells of a Rhesus monkey. The whole condition is sometimes known as *Rhesus or Rh incompatibility*. The Rh factor is similar to the better known A and B factors which determine the blood group and which are the reasons why it is so important that blood transfusions should be carried out only with compatible blood. Occasionally haemolytic disease of the newborn may occur because of incompatibility of other factors—A, B or other rare factors. The Rh factor occurs in about 85 per cent of persons of Caucasian origin. In other racial groups nearly all possess the factor. Individuals possessing the Rh factor are said to be Rh positive; those without are called Rh negative. There are two ways in which an Rh negative woman may develop Rh incompatibility, that is produce Rh antibodies in her blood stream:—transfusion with Rh positive blood or pregnancy with an Rh positive foetus. The blood transfusion is the more effective stimulus; prevention here lies in the exercise of extreme care in the giving of blood transfusions to women. Until the Rh factor was discovered it was not of course possible to do anything at all about this. Pregnancy with an Rh positive foetus will occur in a proportion of Rh negative mothers when the father is Rh positive. The maternal and foetal circulations are in such intimate contact through the placenta that the Rh negative mother can develop specific iso-antibodies to the red cells of her Rh positive foetus. These iso-antibodies then pass through the placenta and act on the red cells and sometimes on the other cells of the foetus. The action on the red cells is to disrupt them. This process is called haemolysis (Greek: *haema* = blood, *lysis* = dissolution). Haemolysis goes on at a slow controlled rate in the normal individual whether adult, newborn or foetus. The red pigment in the blood cells, haemoglobin, is released into the blood stream when the red cells disintegrate; it is then transformed into a yellow pigment called bilirubin. This is disposed of by the normal metabolic processes in the body. In haemolytic disease at any age the destruction of red cells goes on at so rapid a rate that the body cannot cope with the amount of bilirubin produced and a condition of hyperbilirubinaemia results. This stains the tissues, including the skin, and the condition of jaundice occurs (French: *jaune* = yellow). This is why the disease in the newborn has also been called *congenital jaundice*.

Rh incompatibility varies in the severity of its effects on the foetus. The foetus may die in the uterus, resulting in a spontaneous abortion (miscarriage) or a still-birth. The infant may be born alive but survive less than 24 hours. The infant may survive and the condition of kernicterus may occur.

Kernicterus is a hybrid word from the German *kern* (nucleus, kernel), and the Greek *icterus* (jaundice). It was noted very long ago in congenital jaundice that bilirubin might be particularly concentrated in the basal ganglia or nuclei (collections of nerve cells in the brain). It would be more intelligible in English if the term *nuclear jaundice* were used but *kernicterus* is firmly established as the name of the condition.

The infant liver does not have the capacity of the adult liver to metabolise bilirubin and this deficiency is greater when the infant is premature. That is why damage to the brain nuclei occurs in haemolytic disease of the newborn but not in adult jaundice. The mode of action of the bilirubin on the brain cells is not precisely known but it is known that the slightly different bile pigment occurring in obstructive jaundice of the newborn does not cause damage. In obstructive jaundice the disease is not due to the production of an excess of bilirubin but to obstruction of the biliary passages which drain away from the liver the bilirubin formed by haemolysis going on at the slower normal rate.

Kernicterus can occur from causes other than haemolytic disease, especially in premature infants.

As the deafness is due to disease in the nervous pathway from the cochlea to the brain, perceptive deafness is the rule. Loss for high frequencies is characteristic but not invariable. Conductive deafness may occur and one or both ears may be affected. The degree of deafness bears no constant relationship to the severity of the spastic disease. Deafness may easily be overlooked in the presence of severe physical disability, often accompanied by backwardness. These children are so handicapped that every possible help must be given to them and any deafness present must be detected and treated as soon as possible. Examination of the hearing presents special difficulties which L. Fisch has done much to overcome.

Other peri-natal causes
Other peri-natal causes of deafness include anoxia (deficient oxygena-
tion for various reasons) and birth injuries. Prematurity is also
associated with an increased incidence of deafness.

III. POST-NATAL CAUSES

Deafness due to post-natal causes is obviously 'acquired' deafness
(see page 84) but it will be remembered that deafness acquired
before the infant has learnt to speak is similar in its effects to
congenital deafness. Even in older children the effects are more
severe than in adults.

Among the post-natal causes of deafness are inflammation of the
middle ear (acute or chronic otitis media), injury, streptomycin and
other 'ototoxic' antibiotics and general infections due to viruses and
bacteria. Wax in the external auditory meatus causes conductive
deafness and this simple cause must not be forgotten. In some of
these conditions prompt treatment of the underlying condition may
arrest or even reverse the disease process, leaving the child with
an ear that is normal or nearly so. Even when no treatment is
available for the underlying disease process prompt detection makes
it possible to commence auditory training and rehabilitation before
the child has forgotten what he has already learnt of hearing and
speech.

The general infections causing deafness include the common
specific fevers of childhood, especially mumps and measles, inflammation of the brain (encephalitis) or of the covering of the brain and
spinal cord (meningitis). Meningitis may be due to the tubercle
bacillus or to various pyogenic (i.e. pus-forming) organisms of
which the commonest is the meningococcus. The deafness which
may occur in *meningococcal meningitis* is usually bilateral and
severe. Deafness comes on early in the disease, usually before the
end of the first week; rapid commencement of treatment for the
primary disease therefore gives the best chance of preventing deafness.

Deafness following *tuberculous meningitis* was unknown until the
discovery of streptomycin led to the successful treatment of the
disease. Before streptomycin a diagnosis of tuberculous meningitis
was a sentence of death. As streptomycin has a toxic effect on the
ear the deafness may sometimes be due to the cure but in three out
of four cases reported by Whetnall and Lucas in 1952 the acoustic
nerve was involved in tuberculous inflammation. No abnormality
was found in the fourth who had recovered from the meningitis and
died subsequently from acute appendicitis and peritonitis; he was
not deaf.

A. S. Walker, now Deputy Director of the Nuffield Centre, saw
very many cases of deafness following tuberculous meningitis in the

early days of streptomycin treatment. In a paper* he published in 1952 on the first 93 cases he made the following observations on the management of the deafness:—

"The importance of patients being seen as soon as possible after the onset of deafness cannot be sufficiently stressed. Auditory training and lip-reading with the help of an aid must be started at once. Even those who suffer from sub-total deafness with only a little vowel discrimination benefit from the use of an aid, as every sound the patient hears helps in interpreting lip reading. Frequent lessons must be given so that he can associate the new distorted speech patterns he hears with those he previously heard. In addition the aid helps in preserving normal voice tone, and in those with voice changes already present, in rapid improvement. When first tried with a hearing-aid, it is frequently found that there appears to be little benefit. If this is persisted with, there is a gradual improvement in discerning the distorted sounds and the patient derives considerable benefit from the aid.

At the Highgate Unit a teacher of the deaf is employed to start training as soon as deafness is suspected. Daily lessons in auditory training and lip-reading are given, and the results are encouraging. This is not possible in smaller units. In these cases visits are made to the various hospitals to give auditory training and lip-reading instruction. Later, when the patient can be brought to Golden Square by car or ambulance, training is continued there.

The aim is that those patients who have suffered deafness following tuberculous meningitis should later return to a normal school. This is possible in most children of school age if they are seen early. Special rehabilitation units (similar to the one at Golden Square) are urgently required for all such cases. From our experience, intensive training for a period of 6–9 months would fit most cases for returning to a normal school or partially deaf unit."

* *Journal of Laryngology and Otology*, LXVI, pp. 594ff.

CHAPTER VII

DETECTION OF DEAFNESS: TESTS OF HEARING

DETECTION

Early detection of disease is one of the talking points of medicine today. Industrial firms spend freely on routine tests of personnel and health authorities mount screening surveys for the early detection of diabetes, cervical cancer and so on. There is disagreement about the value of some of these routine examinations of apparently healthy people, but on one thing all experts agree: the disabled child has everything to gain from early detection of his disability. The necessity of learning to hear and the special facility for learning in the first three years of life are adequate explanations of the importance of early detection in the case of the deaf born child.

In acquired deafness, too, early detection is important. The disease process may still be going on and it may be possible to arrest it by treatment. Even if this is not possible early treatment may diminish or prevent the resultant disability, for example in the deafness following meningitis (see page 98).

If the possibility of deafness is born in mind its detection in the older child with acquired deafness is usually not too difficult. It is the detection of congenital deafness which presents the greatest difficulties. No one simple test has yet been devised which can determine once for all whether an infant has 'normal hearing' and the individual variations in the development of children make it doubtful if such a test will ever be devised.

Detection depends in the first place on *suspicion*. The best chance of early detection of deafness lies in spreading knowledge of the normal processes of learning to hear, especially of the fact that in the first year of life the infant is learning to listen and to hear. This knowledge needs to be widespread, too, among doctors, nurses, health visitors and others dealing with infants. Too often the parents do suspect deafness quite early, only to find that they cannot get anything done about it. They are incorrectly told that it is impossible to test the child at such a young age, that even if he is deaf nothing can be done about it yet, 'not to fuss', 'just wait and see' and 'all will be well'. All this is so contrary to the truth that it is not surprising that parents are bitter when they eventually realise the truth and that people looking after deaf children develop a crusading zeal.

When Government Departments are so often criticised it is pleasant to record an increase in the number of infants under one year of age referred to the Audiology Unit (now the Nuffield Centre) following the issue in September 1961 of a Ministry of Health Memorandum on *Services for Young Children Handicapped by Impaired Hearing* (Figure VII.1). The graph shows slight increases

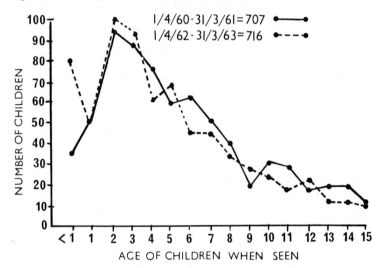

Figure VII.1. Classification by age of new cases referred to the Audiology Unit (Nuffield Centre) before and after propaganda by the Ministry of Health.
(*Reproduced with permission from 'Deafness in Children', Whetnall, in 'Diseases of the Ear, Nose and Throat' (ed. W. G. Scott-Brown, John Ballantyne and John Groves), Butterworths, London.*)

in the number of infants seen in the first three years but the number seen in the first year of life has more than doubled, from 34 to 80. Not all these children were deaf but detection of any defect necessarily involves examination of doubtful cases which turn out to be normal. There is, however, no room for complacency and the deafness of many children is still diagnosed far too late. Constant vigilance by everyone concerned is the only way to successful early detection.

The public—particularly parents—must know that any suspicion of deafness in an infant requires immediate action. The suspicion must be reported and the doctor, nurse, or health visitor who receives the report must take immediate steps to confirm or disprove the suspicion. Sometimes the decision may be obvious, but where there is any doubt the opinion of an expert in child deafness must be sought. If the child's hearing is normal no harm will have been done. On the contrary, it is of positive benefit to remove the parents' anxiety. If the child is deaf, time is all-important. While a decision is delayed the precious days, months, sometimes years of increased facility to learn are slipping away and can never be fully recovered.

One thing must be avoided when there is a suspicion of deafness— frequent tests of hearing by untrained persons. The suspicion may arise from a failure to respond to a loud noise, not because of deafness but because of the normal development of inhibition of the startle reflex (page 28). "He took no notice when the front door banged beside his pram". In the hope that this means nothing, bigger and better sounds are used and as there is still no response, fears of deafness in the mother's mind are confirmed. The type of sound used in such cases is invariably banging of doors, striking fire irons or old tin cans together. This loud noise can only result in a startle reflex at the appropriate age. The fact that the response is inhibited suggests normal hearing, possibly at 6 months and certainly by 8 months.

Sounds with meanings are rarely used in these amateur tests, for once a loud sound has failed to produce a response the parents cannot see how their child can possibly respond to a faint sound, such as his rattle or the sounds connected with food, and so do not try them. Nevertheless, these are the sounds to which there would be a response. Sometimes, however, the worst does happen and these familiar sounds are repeated without the usual reward, just to see if there is a response. If these meaningful sounds are repeated without an association of pleasure the response will become inhibited. This is an inhibition similar to the Pavlovian conditioned response. Anxiety from some incident such as that described above, or the suggestion that perhaps the child is deaf, may lead parents to carry out repeated tests. They may be carried on daily and by the time the child is seen by a doctor he may have ceased to respond to any sounds whatever. Thus the uninformed become certain that the child must be deaf. Yet this child almost certainly has normal hearing. The deaf child does not hear a sound often enough to learn one way or the other, but if he hears a sound he will respond. The inhibited child appears deafer than the deaf.

Rapid expert advice is necessary when the suspicion of deafness is unfounded. The parents may not only be carrying out their amateur tests of hearing; they may also have ceased to talk to their child and be robbing him of essential auditory stimulation. See page 35.

Screening tests

While suspicion by well-informed parents is the first line of detection, there is also a place for screening tests carried out by doctors or medical auxiliaries. It is important that such tests should be carried out early enough and that they should be repeated from time to time. The temptation when organising tests is to postpone the tests to a later age when definite diagnosis is easier, and the whole procedure can be carried out with less effort. This temptation must be resisted because it leads to waste of the invaluable early years of learning. Repetition of tests at intervals is important because some deaf children, especially those with a high-tone loss, may get through the mesh and be 'signed up' as having 'normal hearing'.

Elaborate screening tests are not needed. The aim is not exact diagnosis or assessment of degree of hearing loss. It is *detection*. Tests are carried out with the voice and with loud and quiet sounds. Any marked variation from the responses normal for the baby's age leads to referral to an ear specialist for more detailed testing.

There is no need for special 'deafness detection' sessions. Simple tests of hearing should be included with the other examinations carried out at post-natal clinics, when Health Visitors visit the child at home or when the baby is being examined for any other reason. Mrs. Louise Tracy, founder of the John Tracy Clinic in Los Angeles, described how all sorts of questions were asked when she took John to see doctors. "Does he eat all right?" "Are his bowels regular?" and so on but never any questions directed to his hearing. As a result of work by Mrs. Tracy and others things have improved but there is still a tendency for hearing to be the neglected Cinderella of the special senses.

It is essential that the person carrying out the screening tests should have a good background of knowledge of the process of learning to hear and of the importance of early detection. Exact measurements of hearing are impossible at this age even for the otologist specialising in deafness in children. It follows that no opinion should be expressed by the health visitor or other person carrying out the screening tests, apart from the necessity of an otological opinion. She can help the mother to understand the importance of early training if a defect is present and therefore explain the importance of having an expert decision as soon as possible.

Children 'at risk'

It is known that congenital deafness is liable to occur in certain circumstances, e.g. maternal rubella (German measles), Rh sensitivity, prematurity. It is excellent to have a list of babies 'at risk' for these and other reasons and to take special care in their follow-up. It is important not to restrict follow-up to the 'at risk' babies. As we have seen (page 89) there are still very many cases where the cause of deafness is not known and the babies would not be on the 'at risk' list.

Detection of deafness in older children
In an ideal world all children born deaf would be discovered before they were a year old. As it is, we must consider tests for older children. *At one year* the child should have lost his startle reflex and should localise sounds with which he is familiar. Any deviation from this should lead to a suspicion of deafness. The child of *two years* who fails to understand speech or to talk must also be suspected. From *three to five years* simple speech tests can be used. Measurement of the hearing with an audiometer is quite unsuitable as a screening procedure at this age. Audiometry is not a simple procedure to be learnt in five minutes and applied in two minutes. The voice test is surer, safer and at least as quick. It can be taught quite quickly, whereas audiometry cannot. This is not to say that audiometry is not possible with children of this age, but it requires considerable training and experience in the persons carrying out the test. In the hands of people without adequate training audiometry can produce misleading results and is therefore dangerous.

We now come to the child over *five years*, who should have a hearing test not later than his second term at school. At this age audiometry is feasible and is carried out by audiometricians or by Health Visitors who have received special training in audiometry. Here again, no final decision is taken as a result of the screening test and no opinion should be expressed, other than the need for a specialist examination. This should take place as soon as possible so as to shorten the period of anxiety and enable remedial action to be taken as quickly as possible.

TESTS OF HEARING

The object of this section is not to give detailed instructions about methods of testing hearing, a sort of 'Instant Hearing Test for Amateurs'. Skill and experience are required in the carrying out of the tests and our object is only to give the reader a general idea of the principles involved. It is the principles that matter. There is nothing sacrosanct about the details which will vary from expert to expert and will indeed be under constant review by each expert as his experience and knowledge expands.

Science is based on measurement and there is universal agreement about the desirability of accurate measurement in medicine as in other branches of science. Medicine, however, is also an art and the practising doctor cannot afford to wait until the perfect objective test has been devised. He has to consider the best information available to him and come to a decision about the best treatment for his patient now. There has been a tendency in tests of hearing of young children to adopt a nihilistic attitude. Because the available tests fall short of the highest standards of objective testing of physiological function the temptation is to do nothing and even to scorn those who are prepared to go ahead with the best information they can get. This is a serious cause of delay in the detection and diagnosis of deafness in children—a disastrous delay for the deaf child because he loses the valuable early years of facility to learn.

Research continues on techniques for measurement of hearing in infants which will produce a pure tone audiogram in which the hearing for different pitches of frequencies of sound is expressed in figures. There is, for example, an ingenious and sophisticated technique using an electroencephalograph and a computer in combination with an audiometer. The difficulty remains that even when these techniques have been fully developed they will still produce only pure tone audiograms. They will tell us nothing about the use the brain is making of the information that reaches it from the peripheral hearing mechanism. For this we need the knowledge of the development of learning to hear which has been briefly outlined in Chapter III. In experienced hands the apparently crude tests with loud and faint sounds and the voice give a great deal of information about the presence or not of deafness and about the extent of development of the hearing progress. These developmental tests of hearing fall into line with the developmental tests for all functions devised by Ruth Griffiths and described in *The Abilities of Babies*.

It is important for doctors and parents not to make the mistake of Naaman the leper in his dealings with the prophet Elisha. He was indignant at the simplicity of the proposed cure, the instruction to wash in Jordan. "Behold, I thought," he said, "he will surely come out to me, and stand, and call on the name of the Lord his God, and strike his hand over the place, and recover the leper." In the same way, the uninitiated think "surely the expert will attach the child to a modern instrument and press buttons and produce a piece of paper with figures on it." But all the expert does is to make noises and observe the child. It all seems too crude and simple but in fact it enables the expert to advise on the correct treatment, and this is the object of the tests.

THE OLDER CHILD

About the age of 2 to $2\frac{1}{4}$ years the child is passing into another phase of learning in which different methods of testing may be used. It may be possible to test comprehension for speech; if not, the method used is to to teach the child to make a voluntary movement in response to a sound. The need for an incentive has already been pointed out. This is supplied by making the tests into a game in which the child usually co-operates actively. It is important for the game to be played according to the examiner's rules and not according to a variation produced by the child. Otherwise it deteriorates into a game with no purpose instead of a game in which the child learns he is expected to give a response on hearing a sound.

Tests of hearing for speech

Comprehension of speech becomes slowly more advanced as the child grows older. At one year he may understand a few words, by two years he has begun to understand phrases. After this age he can usually be sat at a low table while he is tested. He is handed a toy suitable for his age and watched to see whether he makes any attempt to play with it or talk about it. If he produces speech any defects in the speech are noted—they may give clues about the hearing. Comprehension of speech is then tested by asking him to do something. Care is taken that he should not be able to lip-read

Figure VII.2. The child's hearing and comprehension of speech is tested
by asking him to pick out an object from the toy farm.
(*Reproduced from 'The Deaf Child'*,
Edith Whetnall and D. B. Fry.
William Heinemann Medical Books, London.)

but must depend entirely on hearing. 'Give the aeroplane to Mother', 'Shut the door' and so on: it will soon be apparent whether any comprehension is present. Between the ages of 2 and 3½ he can be

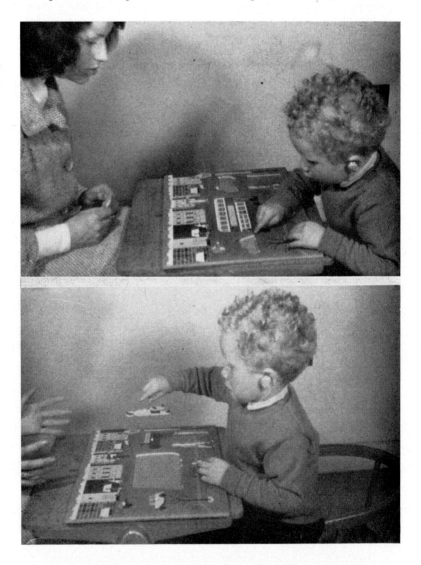

Figure VII.3. The older child's hearing and comprehension can be tested by asking him to pick out a picture of an object.
(*Reproduced from 'The Deaf Child', Edith Whetnall and D. B. Fry. William Heinemann Medical Books, London.*)

asked to point to, or pick up, some object (Figure VII.2). After this age pictures of objects can be used (Figure VII.3). EW's sister, the mother of Janette of Chapter I, was an artist and with the help of the Nuffield Foundation a whole series of cards was produced, each one illustrating a different object or action (see Figure VII.4).

Figure VII.4. These pictures were designed by Phyllis Coupland to illustrate objects and actions (nouns and verbs) and were reproduced in colour with a grant from the Nuffield Foundation. The illustration is taken from one of the artist's line drawings used in the preparation of the blocks.

Conditioned response to sound. The 'Go' Game (see Figure VII.5)

This test is used when there is no hearing for speech. It depends on teaching the child to make a response each time he hears a sound. The response consists in removing a peg from a board or a ring from a pyramid or some similar manipulation with an interesting toy.

To establish the response a noise is made in sight of the child. For example a drum is tapped and the child's mother or some other assistant holds the child's hand and helps him to perform the desired movement each time the sound is made. When he appears to understand he is left alone to do it himself. If he manages this, the drum is taken out of sight to see if he continues to respond. Attention to detail is important. The time interval between the sounds is kept irregular, otherwise the child will automatically make the response at the time interval he has learnt to expect. The drum is gradually taken further away or tapped more softly. When the sound has become too faint and no response occurs it is important to return quickly within the range of the child's hearing. This prevents loss of interest which will impair the responses.

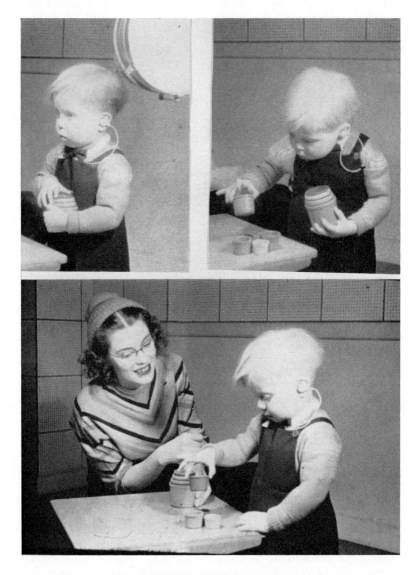

Figure VII.5. The "Go" Game. (see text)
(*Reproduced from 'The Deaf Child', Edith Whetnall and D. B. Fry.*
William Heinemann Medical Books, London.)

Once the method has been learnt any sound may be substituted. The voice is usually the first new sound. 'Go' is often used. The vowel sound 'o' has great intensity and the word has meaning in the context of the game. Then consonants can be substituted. The examiner knows the pitch or frequency level of the different speech sounds and can obtain a useful idea of the child's hearing for different frequencies. The xylophone is also useful for testing pitch discrimination. The sound it produces is not a pure tone and is more interesting to the child than pure tones, which are rather dull. In the early days of the Audiology Unit EW had Boosey and Hawkes make a convenient little xylophone with bars giving frequencies of approximately 256, 500, 1,000, 2,000 and 4,000 cycles per second.

All this has taken quite a long time to describe and it takes longer to do even although the examiner goes as quickly as possible in order to keep up the child's interest. It will not be possible to do all that has been described at the first time of testing; it would be much too boring for the child. The tests can be repeated and expanded at subsequent consultations. Extra information will be acquired about the child's hearing and also about the extent to which he is learning to hear.

Tests with hearing aid
If the tests already done show the presence of deafness the next test is of the response with a hearing aid. Eventually the child will have an individually moulded insert to fit his own ear. To start with a standard ear piece is used. It is inserted into the ear and the aid is switched on quickly but softly. The volume is gradually increased and the mother is asked to call the child's name. A musical box is also valuable as a sound the child will like.

Reactions vary. The child may be pleased. There may be a look of surprise or a great beam of a smile. The child may keep still as though waiting and the volume of the aid should be increased. On the other hand the child may resist all attempts to insert the earpiece. If so, the earpiece is put in the mother's ear and then laid down. Quite often the child will then pick up the aid and want the insert put in his ear.

Occasionally the child bursts into tears but more often will not be separated from the aid. All the tests which have already been described can now be repeated with the aid but it is usually best to put this off to another visit. After all, these tests of hearing are tiring even for an adult.

AUDIOMETRY
Mention has already been made of audiometry which gives a measurement of the intensity of a sound which can just be heard.

There are two main forms of audiometer—the pure tone audiometer and the speech audiometer.

Pure tone audiometry
This test is applied through closely fitting headphones connected to the instrument so that the sound can be delivered to either ear at will. The instrument is able to produce pure tones at different frequency levels, and it can produce them at different levels of intensity. These differences are appreciated as differences in pitch and loudness. When an adult or older child who understands speech is tested he is asked to give an indication each time he hears a sound and when he no longer hears it. For example he may hold up his finger when he hears a sound and put it down again when the sound has gone. The instrument is then set at a particular frequency and the key is pressed to deliver the sound at a particular level of intensity (measured in decibels). The experience of the tester will give him some idea of the intensity level to choose at the beginning. If the person being tested (the 'subject') cannot hear the sound the intensity is increased until there is no doubt that the sound is heard. Then the intensity is lowered in 10 decibel steps until the sound is no longer heard—that is, the intensity is now below the 'threshold' of the subject's ability to hear a sound of this pitch or frequency. The intensity is then increased again but this time in 5 decibel steps, and the procedure goes on up and down, crossing the threshold several times until the examiner is satisfied that he knows the threshold. This has been defined for practical test purposes as the level above which the subject always responds and below which he never or rarely responds. The test is then repeated using a sound at a different frequency until it is possible to produce an audiogram that is a chart which shows the difference in decibels between the subject's threshold of hearing and that of a 'normal' person.

This test is described as subjective because it depends on the reaction of the subject of the test. It is different from an objective test such as, for example, the subject's weight, which depends entirely on the observer's reading of the scale on the weighing machine. Nevertheless, with a trained tester consistent results are obtained in serial tests on the same subject.

The method just described obviously depends on the subject's ability to understand what is required of him. The younger child who does not understand speech needs a different method. Under the age of about $2\frac{1}{2}$ years the child is too immature to co-operate in audiometry. Over $2\frac{1}{2}$ years a modification of the 'Go' game is used. The sounds made by the audiometer take the place of the drum, xylophone, voice and so on; hearing is indicated in the same way by removing a peg or ring or cup from some coloured toy. At first it will

Figure VII.6. Pure tone audiometry using the "Go" Game method.
(*Reproduced from 'The Deaf Child', Edith Whetnall and D. B. Fry.*
William Heinemann Medical Books, London.)

be difficult for the child to concentrate for long on the test but responses to a few frequencies can be obtained and the whole audiogram is slowly built up at later sessions.

To begin with the child's attention will be kept only with loud tones so that the result is not a true threshold result. As the slow process of learning to listen and to hear goes on more accurate results are obtained until in the end one has a true record of the child's threshold for sound. This process takes a considerable time.

Pure tone audiometry can be carried out not only with headphones, i.e. with the sound reaching the ear in the normal way by air-conduction. The sound can also be applied by means of an applicator pressing on the mastoid process of the temporal bone, i.e. by bone conduction. Comparison of the results by air- and bone-conduction may give the otologist useful information about the type of hearing loss.

Speech audiometry

This began with telephone engineers interested in the ability of a telephone system to transmit speech. In clinical speech audiometry the function tested is the ability of the subject to 'hear' speech. Unlike pure tone audiometry the question is not "can the subject just detect that there is a sound?" but "is the speech sound presented in the test intelligible?". Some of the terminology still used derives from the very different purposes of the telephone engineers and may be misunderstood if this is not realised. 'Articulation' in the terms 'articulation tests' and 'articulation scores' is concerned with the ability of the parts of a telephone system to articulate, i.e. to transmit, properly. When the terms are transferred to clinical speech audiometry one may be tempted to think of the subject's ability to 'articulate' or produce speech sounds, as when we say that so-and-so 'articulates' very clearly or very badly. Nothing of this sort is intended; the test is entirely one of speech reception, not of speech production.

The ability that we really want to measure in speech audiometry is the subject's ability to understand continuous meaningful speech. This is difficult to express in figures. It is usual to use lists of isolated syllables, words or sentences. Considerable thought and experimentation has gone into the preparation of such lists or 'test material'. This is usually recorded on a gramophone disc or a tape and is presented to the subject at different intensities, that is, in popular language, different levels of loudness.

The subject is asked to repeat or write down the test material. Suppose a test list of 50 words is used and the subject gets 40 of these correct. The 'articulation score' is said to be 80 per cent. The 'threshold of intelligibility' is sometimes defined as the intensity at which half of the speech presented can be correctly repeated, i.e. when the articulation score is 50 per cent.

The results of speech audiometry are plotted on a graph in which the articulation score is recorded vertically and the intensity of sound in decibels is recorded horizontally, with zero on both scales at the bottom left hand corner of the graph (Figure VII.7). The exact

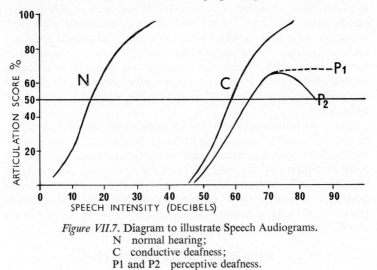

Figure VII.7. Diagram to illustrate Speech Audiograms.
    N   normal hearing;
    C   conductive deafness;
    P1 and P2   perceptive deafness.

results in a normal person vary to some extent with the type of test material used, but in general the articulation scores at different intensities of sound lie along a curve. The patient with impaired hearing will obviously require the sounds to be presented at greater intensities before they are intelligible. That is to say, the whole curve will be further to the right in the deaf patient compared with the normal subject. The exact shape of the curve will depend on the type of deafness. In conductive deafness the curve will be parallel to the normal curve. This means that if we can make the sound loud enough the patient with conductive deafness will get a score of 100 per cent or nearly so. From the description of types of deafness in Chapter VI it will not be surprising that the curve in perceptive deafness has a different shape. Above a certain intensity there is no improvement in intelligibility so that the curve of the articulation scores levels off substantially below 100 per cent. Indeed, in some cases, the score actually gets smaller as the intensity of the sound increases so that the curve bends over and approaches the base line again. The practical application of this is that even the most powerful hearing aid will not allow such a subject to obtain an articulation score of 100 per cent. Fortunately it is still possible to help such a patient because an articulation score of 100 per cent on test material without context is not necessary to enable the patient to follow connected speech in a context. Even isolated sentences are more easily intelligible than isolated words. This is true not only for adults but also for normally hearing children once speech has been acquired. Even while speech is being learnt the meaning of a sentence can be obtained without every word having been understood. This is not so with deaf children who have not yet received adequate auditory training. These children have better hearing for words than for sentences. With adequate training the normal relationship between hearing for words and for sentences develops, so that this test gives an extra means of assessing the adequacy of auditory training.

Like pure tone audiometry speech audiometry can be carried out either with air-conduction or with bone-conduction. It can also be carried out through a hearing aid to obtain a measurement of the assistance given by the aid. The ears may be tested separately or together. Such measurements are used in assessing the value of hearing with both ears as opposed to one ear only and therefore the value of binaural hearing aids instead of a hearing aid in one ear alone.

PSYCHOLOGICAL TESTING

The more intelligent child will be able to make use of clues which have no meaning for the less intelligent. The combination of deafness and mental backwardness creates a great problem. On the other hand the child whose deafness has not been detected may appear 'dumb' in every sense of the word and be considered mentally backward in spite of normal or above average intelligence. The frustration inseparable from lack of communication may present grave problems in behaviour. For all these reasons psychological assessment and intelligence testing are of great importance in the management of the deaf child.

The skilled ear specialist will have made a tentative assessment of the child's psychological make-up and intelligence while testing the hearing. For more accurate estimates the child must be tested by a psychologist with special experience both of normal and of deaf children. Intelligence tests designed for hearing children will give an entirely false impression with deaf children who have not learnt to communicate. It is not enough to add a few points on to the score because of the deaf child's disability. What are needed are special tests designed for the child with absent or grossly defective speech and comprehension of speech. Intelligence tests are validated or standardised by carrying them out on large numbers of children and observing their subsequent progress. Some work has been done on standardisation of tests for deaf children but much more is needed.

As the child receives auditory training and learns to hear, repeated tests of hearing show a progressive improvement. The same improvement occurs with repeated tests of intelligence, so that the results of initial tests should never be regarded as final. The child's real level of intelligence will be at least as high as the initial result; it may well be very much higher.

CHAPTER VIII

AUDITORY TRAINING

"Bathe the child in sound." The advice was given by Dr. Richard Silverman to the grandparents of a boy in Toronto just after the child had been found to be deaf. "That struck me as awfully good commonsense," said the grandfather years later, "and having a rather strident voice myself (my mother was very deaf), I bathed the child in sound and spent all my spare time with him. He was living in our house as his father was overseas in the War."

In spite of the boy's deaf great-grandmother his deafness was not hereditary but due to his mother's having German measles (rubella) in early pregnancy. That is unimportant. What is important is that although he had—and has—a 70 decibel loss of hearing, he acquired the power of natural speech. He owes this to the auditory training he received at home following the advice of Dr. Silverman and of Dr. Wishart, the Toronto ear specialist who was looking after him.

"Bathe the child in sound." That is what happens without deliberate contrivance to the normally hearing baby born into a normal home. *Auditory training* is the conscious provision for the deaf child of the conditions which enable the normally hearing child to learn to 'hear' in the full sense of the word and to produce speech.

The basis of auditory training has been explained in earlier chapters. It depends on two facts—one about the normally hearing child and one about the deaf child. (1) The normally hearing child is not born with fully developed comprehension hearing; he learns this during the early years of life, and there is a special facility to learn during these years. (2) Few, if any, deaf children have absolutely no hearing at all: all, or very nearly all, have at least some residual hearing. The object of auditory training is to enable the child to make the fullest possible use of this residual hearing, which is perhaps better described as 'usable' hearing. Without adequate auditory training this 'usable' hearing becomes useless.

No one but the family at home can provide the constant listening practice, the continuous environment of sound which is essential. All members of the family are important but normally the mother is the key person, the one who spends most time with the child. To play her part properly she needs to add knowledge of the learning process to her existing love for her child and her desire that he should develop as normally as possible. It is she who will do the training of her child. The visits that she and her baby make to the hearing centre or clinic are so that the otologists, audiologists, hearing therapists can teach her what to do, not so that they can act as her substitute in the auditory training of her child. When they live too far away from the centre for frequent attendance they may be best helped by admission for a week or two's concentrated instruction at a Hostel, such as the Hostel for Deaf Babies and their Mothers, opened at Ealing by the Royal National Throat, Nose and Ear Hospital in 1953.

The deaf children who developed 'spontaneous' speech (see Chapter I) show that the activity of the mother is more important than the hearing aid, for none of these children had hearing aids at the time they learnt speech. Nevertheless the hearing aid is a tremendous help. If the mother does not have to apply her mouth to the child's ear the child can see her face and her expression at the same time as he hears her voice. The aid enables him to be much more continually in a hearing environment. He is bathed in the everyday sounds around him as well as hearing his mother's voice when she speaks directly to him from a very close position. He should even sleep with the hearing aid switched on because progress in babbling and learning sound is much more rapid if this is done. By the age when the infant starts to crawl a hearing aid is of even more importance. His ability to crawl tends to remove him from such constant proximity to his mother's voice. Many mothers of deaf babies say that their children babbled until nine months and then ceased. At this age it is essential to fit a hearing aid so that the infant may continue to receive sufficient auditory stimulation.

The task of the mother and the other members of the family is not an easy one. All sorts of difficulties will arise. An important reason for repeated visits to the hearing centre is to prevent these difficulties as far as possible by anticipating them and giving the appropriate advice. The difficulties which arise in spite of this are dealt with as soon as possible after their appearance.

One common difficulty is that the parents feel inadequate. They think of the auditory training as 'education' and feel that it should be given by an 'educationalist'. Sometimes this idea is fostered by well-meaning but ill-informed friends and relations, sometimes even by doctors and others who should know better.

It cannot be too strongly stressed that the acquisition of hearing and speech is not education. It is an essential preliminary which the normally hearing infant acquires before he goes to school to start his education. By the time he reaches school he has already acquired a basic vocabulary and the knowledge of how words are put together to form sentences. The object of auditory training is to give the deaf child the opportunity to do the same.

Much patience is needed and the parents need to remember and to be reminded how long the normally hearing child takes to learn to hear and to talk. It is not reasonable to expect the deaf child to learn more rapidly, but the natural anxiety of the parents may make the time seem longer. In reckoning the progress of their child they must calculate from the date auditory training commenced and not from the date of the baby's birth. Another object for the visits to the hearing centre is so that the otologists can encourage the parents by pointing out the progress that is being made in learning to hear.

The parents need to realise the need for constant repetition. Sounds are not learned the first time they are heard. They need to be heard over and over again. Some parents find it easier than others. Some feel self-conscious about talking to their child because he is deaf and it makes them feel foolish. They need encouragement and coaching in what to say and do. Everything done for the baby must be accompanied by speech. "Now we're going to give baby his bath" or "his drink" or whatever it is and so on and on. Singing comes into it too—nursery rhymes, lullabies, anything. Always associated with the sounds are the pleasures of being fed, of being held securely, of being addressed in a loving tone of voice—all this facilitates the learning process. Gradually the baby learns to discriminate between sounds. Vowel sounds are the first speech sounds for which discrimination will be learnt and this will be shown when the baby starts to imitate the sounds. Notes and recordings of the sounds as they appear make a valuable record of progress and are an encouragement to the parents to persevere. There should, however, be no attempt to teach particular sounds as such. Isolated speech sounds are dull and meaningless. Words, phrases and sentences must be heard in association with their meanings.

Eventually the baby will start to produce speech. This must be encouraged, not only by expressions of pleasure but by repeating the sounds the child produces, making them into sentences. The child's first attempts at speech are crude, understandable only by the loving parents. As the words are repeated correctly the child has a chance to bring his own production of sound closer and closer to the normal speech of the community in which he lives. The parents do this automatically with the normally hearing child. One could multiply examples from one's observation of the infants one sees and hears as one goes about one's ordinary existence. Walking by the seashore—"Ee uh" says the infant. "Yes, darling," replies the mother "look at the seagulls. What a lot of seagulls on the waves." Another example was overheard in a café. "Oo aw" utters the small infant, holding aloft a foot clad in a beautiful new red wellington boot. "No," says mother, "we're not going to take your boots off now."

As the child grows older, two years and onwards, toys and pictures can be used to help with auditory training and the building of a

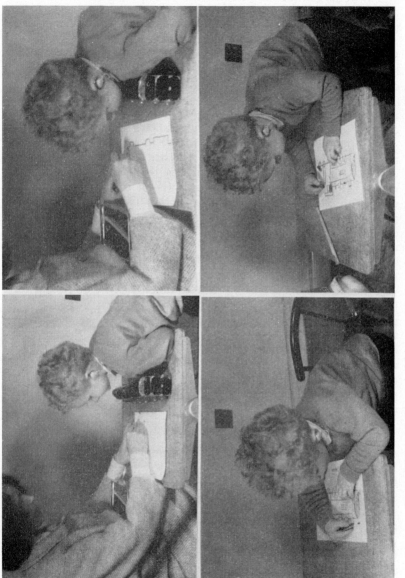

Figure VIII.1. Mother and child co-operate in a drawing as he learns some new words.
(*Reproduced from 'The Deaf Child', Edith Whetnall and D. B. Fry. William Heinemann Medical Books, London.*)

vocabulary. Drawings made on the spot help to illustrate the meanings of words and the child can join in and help (Figure VIII.1). If the parents have artistic talent it is a help but the primary object is to illustrate the meaning of the words, not to produce works of art.

Great help can also be obtained from learning to read. There has been publicity recently about the advantages for all children of learning to read at an early age. It certainly is a great help for the child with a hearing loss.

Attendance at a day nursery with normally hearing children is invaluable. The child learns to mix with other children. The other children are also an excellent source of speech sounds. Children speak loudly and simply. They do not have to bend down to bring their voices close to the deaf child. They are all at the same level anyway. Adults learning a foreign language realise how helpful it is to listen to children talking, and this is even more obvious for the child's learning of speech. Attendance at a nursery also gives the mother a rest from the constant anxiety of caring for her deaf child and she is encouraged by seeing him learning to hold his own and to mix with other children. Eventually entry into the world of school will be made much easier for the child by previous attendance at a day nursery.

After about two years of age it is essential to set aside definite times, say two short periods each day, for going over words and phrases. This is not formal training. It is a modification of what the normally hearing child comes to love and demand—the exact repetition of a story day in and day out. As the author of *Jock of the Bushveld* writes about his own little children: "To such an audience a story may be told a hundred times but it must be told, as Kipling says, 'Just So', that is, in the same way." The deaf child needs this repetition even more than his hearing brothers and sisters, not less.

AUDITORY TRAINING WHEN DEAFNESS IS DIAGNOSED LATE

The basic principles of training are the same but everything will be more difficult. The child may have heard so few sounds that sound has acquired no meaning; he has indeed almost learned to ignore sound. In addition the years of extra facility in learning are slipping past. The inability to communicate brings frustration and behaviour problems. Because sound is meaningless it may be difficult to get him to wear an aid. The parents must work harder and give the child the extra auditory training he needs if he is to make the grade and overcome his disability. The child who has normal hearing or the deaf child who has received early auditory training has acquired a great deal of general knowledge as well as a basic vocabulary. The child whose deafness is first diagnosed at the age of 3 or 4 years is becoming retarded in general learning and may appear dull as well as presenting behaviour problems.

The parents and everyone else dealing with such a child must remember the long years of listening and learning to hear that lie behind the normally hearing child before he goes to school. The deaf child diagnosed late must not be pitchforked into school before he has had a chance to make up the lost years of listening. It is better for him to go to school a year late than to be sent at the 'correct' age to a special school to be taught by methods which do not use the hearing and which will not prepare him for life in a hearing community. The length of time necessary must be appreciated not only by the parents but by the planners of education programmes. A good partially deaf unit may be a valuable stepping stone for some of these children. This is a unit for partially deaf children in a hearing school. The children receive special attention in the unit but mix with the normally hearing children for games, physical training and so on. The success of these units depends on the staff. The ratio of staff to children must be sufficient to allow individual attention and the staff must be imbued with the aim of transferring the child to the ordinary school as soon as possible. Teachers in such partially deaf units and in schools for the deaf need great self-effacement to make them push their most successful pupils on as quickly as possible away from themselves and into a normal hearing environment.

THE DEAF CHILD IN A HEARING SCHOOL

It is a great moment when a deaf child succeeds in entering a hearing school but this is not the end. He must not be left to sink or swim on his own. Parents, otologists, hearing therapists can do a tremendous amount to prepare the way for the child by interviewing the head teacher and other teachers and helping them to understand the special problems of the deaf child. The progress of one child was retarded for a whole term by a teacher who treated her as 'a silly little deaf child'. Problems are bound to arise and each must be dealt with as quickly as possible.

CHILDREN WITH MULTIPLE HANDICAPS

It is generally accepted nowadays that the child with a disability benefits from being kept in the normal community if this is at all possible. The deaf child with average intelligence who starts auditory training early can usually learn to hold his own in a hearing en-vironment. If the diagnosis is made very late or if the child has some other disability as well his chances are less. If, for example, he is of less than average intelligence or is blind or has cerebral palsy he has far greater handicaps to overcome. Special schooling, sometimes even in a residential institution, may be necessary. Each child's requirements must be individually assessed. The education needs to be tailor-made, not ready-made, and the greatest co-operation is required from all concerned.

CHAPTER IX

HEARING AIDS

Very little knowledge of the internal combustion engine is necessary in order to drive a car and the user of a hearing aid does not need to know much about acoustics and electronics. Both the car driver and the hearing aid user, however, will be likely to get a better performance from the machines they use if they have some knowledge of what is going on under the bonnet or inside the case of the hearing aid. When a child is the user of the hearing aid it is the parents who need this elementary knowledge.

The hearing aid is a device to amplify sound. Various forms of *mechanical* hearing aid have been used for centuries. Essentially these are tubular instruments with a wide end to collect sound and a narrow end for insertion into the ear hole (external auditory meatus). They include ear trumpets and speaking tubes. Vanity and the desire to conceal a disability led to all sorts of curious devices such as the incorporation of hearing aids in fans and walking sticks (Figure IX.1). The modern electrical hearing aid concealed in the frame of spectacles has a long line of mechanical predecessors.

Goldstein, a great collector of old hearing aids, tells us that the first *electrical* hearing aid was produced by Alt in Vienna in 1900. It was called the 'micro-telephone' and really all electrical hearing aids are based on the telephone idea. The microphone or receiver converts sound waves into electrical impulses, the impulses are magnified in the amplifier, and the amplified electrical impulses are converted back into sound waves in the telephone or ear piece. The earliest aids were of the carbon type. With the invention of thermionic valves great improvements in performance were possible but the instruments were very bulky. In the 1930's midget valves made it possible to produce really wearable aids. The invention of transistors has made all previous hearing aids of historical interest only, because of the lightness, small size and low running costs of the transistor aid.

It is useful to have some idea of the meaning of some of the *technical terms* used in discussing hearing aids. The *performance* of an aid has been defined as the degree to which the aid can make the hearing of a deaf person more nearly normal. The performance depends on the *characteristics* of the aid. These characteristics are measured objectively and a variety of tests has been devised to do this. The *specification* of the aid describes which tests have been used and the exact conditions under which they were carried out.

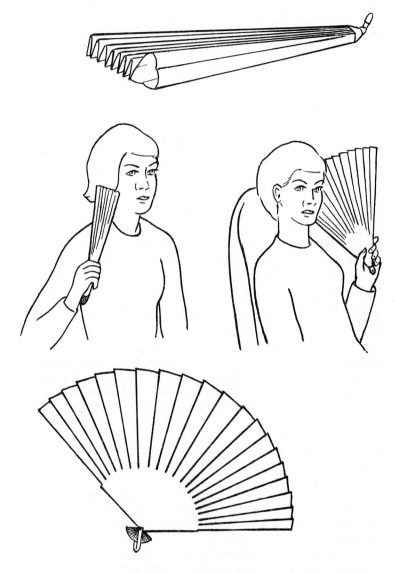

Figure IX.1. The acoustic fan—an old method for camouflaging a mechanical hearing aid.
After 'Problems of the Deaf', Goldstein, Laryngoscope Press, St. Louis.

Various organisations have laid down standards to which hearing aids must conform.

An aid which gives a satisfactory performance with these objective tests must finally be tested with the patient. Speech is the most important of the sounds to which man listens and the aid must therefore be tested for its ability to improve the deaf individual's ability to recognise speech. By speech audiometry (see Chapter VII) this ability can be expressed in figures. The test is nevertheless subjective and cannot be carried out on a child who has not yet learned to hear and talk, at least to some extent. Results obtained from older children who have used hearing aids must therefore be applied in making a decision in the case of an infant or young child not yet able to talk.

CHARACTERISTICS OF A HEARING AID
Amplification or acoustic gain
This is the increase in sound produced by the amplifying system in the aid. This is measured in decibels (db.). A gain of up to 80 db. may be necessary but it must be at least 40 db. or weak sounds will not be heard. Much of the information used in recognising consonants comes from weak sounds in the upper frequency range of hearing, the area first damaged in perceptive or nerve deafness. The ability of an aid to amplify weak sounds is referred to as its *sensitivity*.

Output
This must be carefully distinguished from amplification or gain. The terms are very readily confused. *Gain* is the difference between the intensity of the sound entering the aid and the sound delivered by the aid to the user. *Output* is the maximum intensity of the sounds which it is possible for the aid to deliver. Limitation of the output is important for various reasons. If amplification is allowed to take place regardless of the intensity of the sounds reaching the hearer the output of the aid may reach a level which causes discomfort or actual pain. Up to a point the ability to recognise and understand speech improves as the intensity of the sound increases. In the normal individual this point is about 65 db.; above this level further increases in intensity produce little or no improvement. At a level of 110 to 135 db. sound will be difficult to understand as well as uncomfortable or painful. For these reasons the output of an aid is limited usually to a level of about 115 to 120 db. although a lower level may be needed in some types of deafness. This limitation is present in the amplifier and is not under the control of the user.

The conflicting needs of high gain and limitation of output are related to the fact that some speech sounds are louder than others by as much as 30 db. This difference may be increased in deafness especially when high frequency hearing is lost. To make the faint high frequency sounds loud enough would result in over-amplification of the lower frequencies. Selective limitation of the output of these lower frequencies is therefore necessary.

Methods of limiting output
Output can be limited by peak clipping or by automatic volume control, sometimes called automatic gain control. These methods may be combined in the same aid.

Peak clipping
This describes the method exactly. Limitation of sound is achieved by cutting off the peaks of sound waves which are too great (Figure IX.2 (*b*)). Vowel sounds are louder than consonants and so the

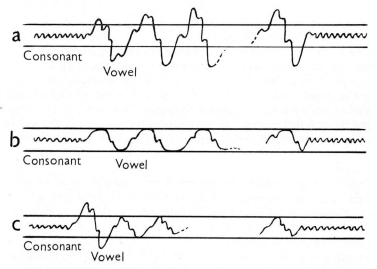

Figure IX.2. Representation of speech sounds in wave form:— (*a*) normal; (*b*) effect of peak clipping—the peaks are cut off; it is the vowel which is affected, the consonant is unaffected and speech is intelligible although distorted; (*c*) effect of compression—no distortion; speech remains perfectly intelligible—the compression effect takes place 0.0001 to 0.002 second after the loud sound is incident on the amplifier.
(*Reproduced with permission from 'Hearing Aids', Whetnall, in Diseases of the Ear, Nose and Throat (ed. Scott-Brown), Butterworths.*)

sound waves are of greater amplitude. This means that the vowel sounds are clipped more than the consonants. This results in some distortion of the speech.

Automatic volume control
This involves a circuit designed so that loud noises automatically reduce the amplification or gain of the hearing aid. This is also

called 'compression amplification'. The shape of the sound waves is not deformed and the speech is not distorted (Figure IX.2 (c)). Automatic volume control (A.V.C.) is slightly more expensive than peak clipping but for many users it is worth the extra expense. Some users of hearing aids without A.V.C. can be seen to be constantly fiddling with the volume controls of their aids. When the gain is low they fail to hear weak speech sounds so they increase the volume. Then they find that loud speech and noise cause distortion and even discomfort so they turn the volume control down again. For such users automatic volume control is a great boon because it does automatically and efficiently what they are failing to do manually. In some children A.V.C. may make all the difference between success and failure in learning to hear. The expense is very small compared with the expense of special schooling which may be necessary if the child fails to acquire the skill of hearing.

A criticism formerly brought against automatic volume control was that the ear was not protected against loud sounds during the time that the A.V.C. took to come into effect. This has been overcome by reducing the delay in onset of A.V.C. to as little as 0·001 or 0·002 second.

The frequency range

The frequency range of a hearing aid is the range of frequencies which the aid amplifies. It should extend from 250 to 4,000 cycles per second. With a narrower range intelligibility is affected even for children who appear not to have hearing for the whole frequency range when tested with the pure tone audiometer.

The frequency response curve

The frequency response curve of the aid is the way in which the amplification varies for each frequency. The idea of matching the frequency response curve to the exact hearing loss is obviously attractive, on the analogy of tailoring the spectacle lens to the error of refraction of the eye. Many independent investigations have however shown that the most satisfactory curve for most types of deafness in adults is a substantially flat curve or one rising by 6 db. per octave from 700 cycles per second. In children it is different and various types of aid are preferred. For the severely deaf child a flat response is usually more satisfactory, probably because more amplification is obtained. The child with a high tone loss, not surprisingly, prefers a high-frequency boost. For some, in addition, peak clipping or suppresion of the low frequencies is desirable.

FUNCTION AND FALLACIES IN THE USE OF HEARING AIDS

The hearing aid is only a machine and its sole function is to amplify sound. This seems obvious but as with many other treatments in medicine some magic is expected. Adequate time is not allowed and the aid is discarded in disappointment because it has not produced instant speech or some other impossible result that was expected.

It was pointed out in Chapter III that learning to hear cannot take place if the sounds heard are not loud enough. This is the deaf child's problem. The hearing aid amplifies speech sounds and makes them loud enough but the deaf child will not instantly learn to hear, any more than the normally hearing infant who needs a year or so of listening practice before the production of his first word. The deaf child will need at least as long a period of listening before he has progressed sufficiently in learning to hear to enable him to begin to comprehend and then to produce speech.

One point which causes concern to some people is the thought that the speech the deaf child hears is 'distorted'. Some forms of deafness do produce considerable distortion as well as attenuation of sound. This may be a great problem to the adult who becomes deaf and to the child who becomes deaf after he has learnt to hear and to speak. The congenitally deaf child has no standard of learnt sounds with which to compare the sounds that he starts to hear through his hearing aid. It does not matter that these sounds are different from those that the rest of us hear. What does matter is that he should learn a code of sound signals associated with their meanings. These sounds may be 'distorted' for us but it is essential to realise that they are not 'distorted' for the child born deaf.

Distortion is a problem for the child with acquired deafness, the child who goes deaf, often suddenly, after he has learnt to hear and to speak. A description has already been given (page 98) of the vital importance of early fitting with a hearing aid and early auditory rehabilitation in such cases.

Fear of acoustic trauma
One of the most dangerous fallacies about hearing aids is the fear of damage to the hearing from acoustic trauma due to the amplified sounds delivered to the ear by the aid. This fear is entirely without foundation. Acoustic trauma is a real enough condition. Noise can damage the hearing but the type of noise involved is either long exposure (e.g. in a factory) to continuous noise of high intensity (over 100 db.) or a sudden explosion such as gun-fire. Speech sounds, even with the most powerful hearing aid, are never delivered continuously at an intensity of 100 db. Speech sounds are not a continuous sound but change in frequency and intensity from second to second. The mentally normal child will rapidly indicate his discomfort if exposed to too much amplification. Even education-ally subnormal children will not tolerate too loud a sound.

It is possible that the myth of acoustic trauma from hearing aids arose from the observation of isolated cases of progressive deafness, that is cases in which the deafness becomes progressively worse, not due to an outside agency but to the nature of the disease process. Sometimes this type of deafness runs in families and the story of a brother and sister illustrates the fallacy of attributing deterioration in hearing to the use of a hearing aid in such cases. The sister, aged 4, had had an aid for $1\frac{1}{2}$ years when her hearing started to show some deterioration. She had started to talk by this time. Deterioration of hearing due to acoustic trauma takes place in the ear, in the peripheral hearing mechanism. Even if the deterioration in this girl's hearing had been due to the hearing aid, she was obviously better off as she was than if she had been left without a hearing aid. She had slightly more impaired peripheral hearing which she had learnt to use in the comprehension and production of speech. Without the aid even slightly better peripheral hearing would have been of no practical use to her because she would never have heard sounds loud enough for them to have acquired any meaning for her.

The history of her younger brother showed that the hearing aid was not the culprit. He had been found to be deaf at the same time as his older sister. This was very many years ago and it was erroneously thought that he was rather young to have a hearing aid. Without an aid his hearing showed a steady deterioration more severe than that of his sister. Clearly they were examples of familial progressive deafness and not of deterioration of hearing due to hearing aids. A few years later when aids were being fitted on younger children both the brother and the sister would have received aids and it would not have been possible to determine the true cause of the deterioration in hearing.

Fears about damage by hearing aids to the peripheral hearing mechanism must not be allowed to divert attention from the beneficial effect of the aid on the full comprehension hearing which develops when the child has learnt to hear. This is the reason why this matter has been discussed so fully. The parent—even sometimes the professional adviser involved—who is terrified of acoustic damage will always be turning the volume control of the aid down; perhaps the aid will be taken off completely for long periods. This is a hopeless situation. The child does not hear sounds 'loud enough' and 'often enough' (page 37) for learning to take place. The aid will be assumed to have failed when in fact it has never been used properly.

Other fallacies about the use of hearing aids have already been mentioned but they are still so widespread that they warrant listing and comment:—

(i) that the aid must not be used on infants under 36 weeks—sometimes even 2 years is mentioned as the appropriate age; this delay wastes the invaluable early months of facility in learning.

(ii) that any aid is good enough and that it is the fault of the child, of the mother, of the method, if the child fails to make progress; on the contrary if the child fails to progress the first thing to consider is the type of hearing aid. Perhaps automatic volume control is needed; perhaps amplification is insufficient. A change to the right aid results in dramatic improvement.

(iii) that the aid is of no value for the deaf born child if he does not understand immediately he has the aid—this ignores all that we know about the time required for the listening and learning process.

(iv) that a hearing aid will prevent the child's learning to lip-read; in fact it facilitates the learning of lip-reading.

(v) that a large percentage of deaf born children are totally deaf; it is doubtful if any are totally deaf. Certainly all should have the benefit of an adequate trial with a hearing aid. 'Adequate' means with a suitable aid, under the right environmental conditions and for a length of time comparable to the time taken by the normally hearing child to acquire speech. Many children who are thought to be totally deaf will benefit from such a trial and will be found to have appreciable amounts of residual hearing.

CHOICE OF A HEARING AID

The hearing aid should be designed so that it will help the deaf child as much as possible and cause as little trouble as possible. It must therefore be *small, light, robust and easily wearable.*

The early Medresco aid with its bulky batteries was a great advance on no aid at all but *the monopack experiment* carried out in 1952 with T. S. Littler showed the tremendous advantages of the small light aid with the batteries incorporated in the same case as the amplifier. These aids were supplied at a reduced charge by one of the commercial hearing aid firms and paid for with voluntary contributions to the 'Golden Square Fund'. There was no difficulty in getting the young child to wear a small light aid and the scope of the experiment was extended from babies to include older maladjusted children whose only hope of remaining in a hearing environment in an ordinary school was to have an aid they were willing to wear and use continuously. In course of time a monopack Medresco aid was produced. *Automatic volume control* is essential whenever there is evidence of intolerance to sound or recruitment. In young children it is impossible to say whether intolerance and recruitment are present so that they should always have aids with automatic volume control.

Types of aid (Figure IX. 3. (*a*), (*b*), (*c*) **and** (*d*)

The choice of the right aid for each child depends on consideration of all the facts of the case. There are two main types. The *body aid with a lead* has the microphone, the amplifying system, and the small battery all housed in a case which is worn in a pocket or in a harness on the body. A flexible lead connects this to the telephone in the ear mould which fits in the patient's external auditory meatus. This type of aid gives greater amplification than the ear level aid (see below). In spite of its obvious disadvantages it must be chosen for the child who needs greater amplification than the ear level aid can supply.

The *ear level aid* is worn behind the ear between the lobe of the ear and the skull. It is neat in appearance and comfortable to wear. It is quite secure and does not fall off during games or in the gymnasium. There is greater freedom in head movements without a lead. The microphone which picks up the sound is in the immediate vicinity of the ear. This arrangement is obviously closer to the normal than the body aid and carries certain acoustic advantages:—

(i) the sound patterns received have been modified by the diffraction effects of the head rather than of the body;

(ii) in the desirable use of aids in both ears the two ear-level aids constitute pick-up points roughly equivalent to the ears.

The only disadvantage of the ear level aid is that it gives less amplification than the body aid. It is therefore unsuitable when great amplification is needed.

Hearing aids incorporated in a *pair of spectacles* should be considered only when both spectacles and hearing aids are needed. The hearing aids make the spectacles heavy. To wear them with plain glass and normal vision is just pandering to the idea that defective vision is acceptable, but defective hearing is something shameful.

Bone conduction aids may be required prior to operation for a child with congenital narrowing or absence of the ear hole (congenital meatal stenosis or atresia). L. Fisch showed that the ordinary type of air conduction aid with an insert can be used even in a discharging ear.

Binaural Hearing Aids

The man with the monocle excites immediate attention. The ophthalmologist who prescribed only a monocle for a patient with defective vision in both eyes would be regarded as a little odd. The situation is completely opposite with hearing aids. Here the tradition has been to prescribe only one aid. It is probable that the origin of this tradition lies in expense but it is now so hallowed by custom that

(i)

(ii)

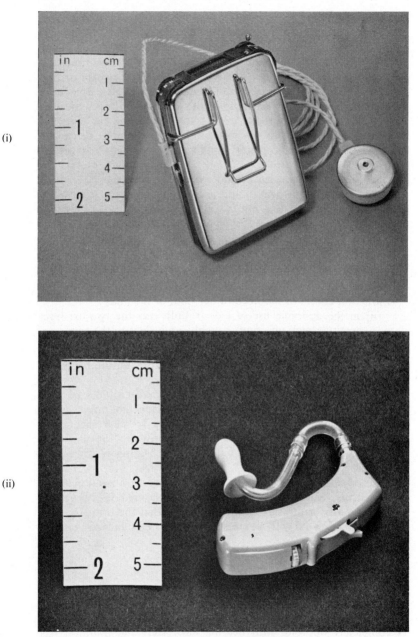

Figure IX.3 (*a*)(i) Small transistor body-worn aid (Siemens 335 Sirefon Extra); (ii)
Ear level aid (Philips KL 6730).
(*Reproduced with permission from Test Reports of the Technical Laboratory of
the Royal National Institute of the Deaf.*)

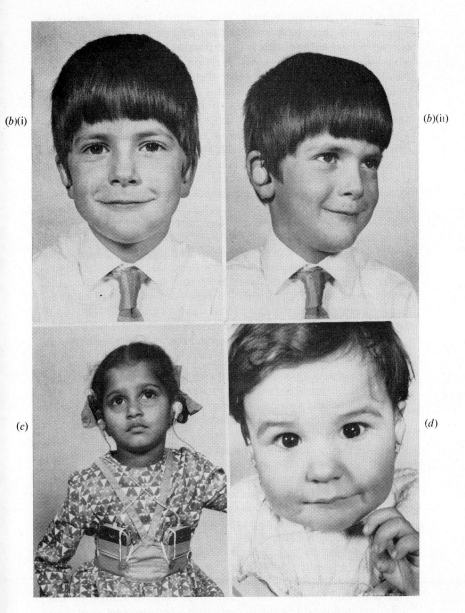

Figure IX.3 (b), (c) and (d). Children with binaural hearing aids.
(b) Boy with two ear level aids which are not easily seen in the full face view.
(c) Girl with two body aids worn in a harness.
(d) Baby, aged eleven months, with two body aids worn in a small harness.

advocates of binaural hearing aids are told they must produce evidence that these have an advantage over monaural aids. As the normal person is born with two functioning ears the onus of proof would seem to lie in the other direction and the advocates of the monaural hearing aid should prove their case.

The advocates of binaural hearing do however have plenty of facts to support their views. Localisation of the source of sound (distance as well as direction) is better with two ears than with one. The ability to localise has far reaching effects in the understanding of complex sounds, especially speech. It enables the hearer to discriminate between foreground and background sounds. Sound is given perspective. Binaural hearing is necessary for the normal ability to pick out sounds of importance in unfavourable situations, for example where there is much background noise. It also enables the hearer to distinguish the separate speakers when several people are talking at the same time.

All of this has been worked out experimentally. Clinical experience with binaural hearing aids tells the same tale. Nearly all users report subjective benefits; in children too young to describe the improvement, significant changes in behaviour are noticed with the change from one to two aids. These changes occur not only with ear level aids which are ideal, but also with aids worn on the body.

Here are three examples of the evidence of improvement with binaural hearing aids:

1. The first is quoted from a paper* read by EW at the First British Academic Conference in Otolaryngology in 1963:— "Another study was carried out on a group of eight children in a partially deaf unit of the William Morris School. I am grateful to Mr. Pegg, the headmaster, who keeps full and careful details of learning processes, hearing and speech in these children. Improvements were noticeable in every child: they were easier to teach, learnt more easily, heard more easily. A series of speech tests were carried out and showed an improvement against the monaural scores in six who had enough speech to test in this way. The other two did not have enough speech for verbal tests. They are improving more rapidly than would have been expected with one aid. The children like their aids and are oral in attitude."

2. Speech audiometry can be carried out in older children with an apparatus which makes it possible to test either ear separately or both ears together. One group of 20 children studied by EW showed improved hearing in every case when two ears were used. In three cases the improvement was slight but in three there was a 15 decibel shift at the 50 per cent level in the articulation score.

---

* *The Journal of Laryngology and Otology*, Vol. LXXVIII, p. 1084.

This means that 15 decibel less amplification is needed for understanding if both ears are used instead of only one. Improvement was shown both by children with a flat loss on the pure tone audiogram (i.e. the same degree of loss for all frequencies) and by those with a loss mainly for the high frequencies.

Figure IX.4 shows the speech audiogram of a boy who became deaf from meningitis at 15 months. The pure tone audiogram

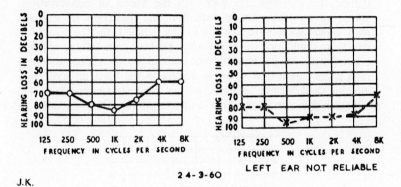

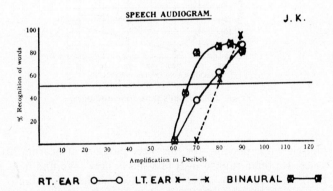

Figure IX.4. Speech and pure tone audiograms showing advantage of binaural hearing compared with hearing in each ear separately. The 50% score shows an improvement of nearly 15 decibels.
(*Reproduced with permission from 'Binaural Hearing', Whetnall, Journal of Laryngology and Otology, Volume LXXVIII.*)

shows a slightly curved loss of 70 db. in the right ear and a loss of 80 to 90 db. in the left. He has normal speech. Two aids have helped this child to achieve excellent discrimination. The 50 per cent score shows nearly 15 db. improvement.

3. Figure IX.5 shows the audiogram of a boy whose mother wrote to EW after he had been fitted with two commercial hearing aids:— "My husband and I would like to thank you very much for your efforts in getting John his two commercial aids. He has been wearing them for a couple of weeks now and really the change is remarkable. He hears and understands everything the first time now whereas before we had to get his attention, then deliver the message. He picks up the theme of conversations which have nothing to do with him and interrupts us with his own observations. He also picks up words from the television which he could not do previously. To hear him talking to (and arguing with) his younger brother is a real joy, as you can imagine. It is unfortunate that when he comes to the Unit he goes back into his shell because at home we just can't stop him talking. He talks all day about anything and everything. He even talks to

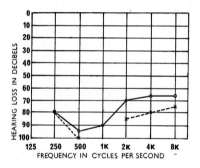

Figure IX.5. John's pure tone audiogram.

himself while playing, for the sheer pleasure of hearing his own voice. He often says to us 'I talk nicely now'. We find he is much more relaxed with other people too as he understands their questions first time off and once he has replied the ice is broken.

The last time we saw you I was a bit worried because we couldn't get John to wear his Medrescos all day. The change came when we had two 10 year old boys to stay with us for two weeks. All the time they were here John forgot about his aids and he got so used to hearing things that he continued to wear them after the boys left. Now, when he takes his aid off he says immediately 'I can't hear you now', and his speech becomes slightly imperfect. You must have heard this kind of tale many times before, but I thought you might like to know what brought the change about. Lastly, he can localise sound pretty well now."

Y-leads

A cheaper method of using both ears is to have a single body aid with a Y-shaped lead conveying the amplified sound to inserts in both ears. Experience shows that learning proceeds more rapidly with this system than when the amplified sound is delivered only to one ear. The impulses from the two ears are added together or 'summated'. The Y-lead, however, is only a second-best. The user loses the advantages of localisation and the ability to distinguish important sounds from the background of unwanted noise. In EW's experience every young child who got the chance to have two aids liked them.

OTHER METHODS OF AMPLIFYING SOUND

The auditory trainer

This is a powerful desk or table amplifier which provides far greater amplification than even the most powerful wearable hearing aid. Its chief value is in the stage of learning to hear. At this time sound needs to be heard far louder than will be necessary once the meanings of the sounds have been learnt. The disadvantage is the size of the trainer which means that it is not portable and can be used only for limited periods of auditory training. This can, however, be very useful as a supplement to the child's continuous listening throughout the day through his own individual hearing aid.

Induction Loop System

In this system an amplifier is connected to a loop of wire. An induction coil in a specially adapted hearing aid picks up the electrical impulses from the loop. The amplifier is connected to the teacher's microphone. In this way the child has the benefit of amplified speech from the teacher without being encumbered by wires.

CONCLUSION

The mothers described in Chapter I found out for themselves the value of early auditory training. They achieved their successes without the use of hearing aids. With modern binaural hearing aids from the moment of diagnosis their children would have been even more successful but it is important to remember that the most perfect hearing aid is useless without the loving persistent adult to provide an environment of sounds repeated over and over again in association with their meaning. The hearing aid can do nothing by itself but with the help of the hearing aid the mother can help her handicapped child to learn to hear.

EPILOGUE

—The Editor—

I found the letter quoted on page 136 among Edith Whetnall's papers. She had received it not very long before her sudden death. It was so good a description of the benefits of suitable binaural aids that I asked the mother's permission to publish it. In replying she gave me news of John's progress. Once again the writing is so descriptive and touches so many of the points stressed in this book that I decided to print the following extracts as an epilogue. They show some of the opposition which still exists to the auditory approach in the training of severely deaf children. More important they show what a handicapped child can do when he has intelligent, loving, persistent parents who are given the right advice.

"John is living proof of just how right your wife was in her approach to deafness and we shall always be grateful to her for putting us on the road to success. We were fortunate enough to hear one of her lectures and at the same time a lecture by Professor Fry and over coffee we briefly explained John's problem and your wife advised us to go ahead with normal nursery school leading to normal primary school education and to steer clear of partial hearing units at least until John had been given the chance to develop normally. She also gave us the necessary courage to go against the County Council policy (with her backing of course) and since making that decision (which at the time was quite a formidable one) we and John have never looked back. We managed to keep good relations with the County. We have tolerated a succession of teachers for the deaf from the County Council and each in turn has insisted on subjecting John to more hearing tests simply because no-one can accept that John is as deaf as we say he is, yet has overcome his handicap to such a tremendous extent. We lose no time in pointing out that we followed the Whetnall-Fry method to the letter and I know many of these teachers have had to think again.

At $3\frac{1}{2}$ years of age he was given two Medrescos and began catching up the lost years by a constant bombardment of speech from us. He learned to read many words before he used them in speech and fairly romped through the Ladybird Reading Series. At 4 he received the two commercial aids and his hearing, comprehension and general well-being took a great leap forward. He attended normal nursery school two mornings a week then

138

and we began to break down his reserve. By the time he was 5 his social problem was far greater than his hearing or speech problem. I had indexed an active vocabulary of 1,200 words (another Whetnall idea) so was able to show the authorities what he could say, even if he was too shy to speak to them during an appointment. *All* his speech has been and still is acquired *spontaneously* and it is for this reason that he has such a wide range of words, and expressions. We know that the language he has and the love of language and reading could only have been acquired (or lost) in those early years at home and we thank God we had the fortune to meet Miss Whetnall at such a critical time because without her advice (and her book *The Deaf Child*) we should have blindly followed the County Council policy and our son would be a very different person from the one he is now. I think it is more accurate to describe him as a normal 7 year old who doesn't always hear you first time and says 'What?' quite often than a severely deaf child who has normal speech, behaviour and social life."

INDEX

Accent, 57
Acoustic information, 40, 44
Acoustic nerve, 13, 17
Acoustic trauma, unwarranted fear of, 128–9
Acquired deafness, 84–5, 97–8
  age of onset, 84
  speed of onset, 84–5
Amateur tests of hearing, 101
Analogy in learning of language, 62–3
Anoxia, as cause of deafness, 97
Aphasia, motor, 21
Articulation score, 112–14
Ascertainment of deafness, 3
Association areas of cerebral cortex, 21
Audibility, threshold of, 86
Auditory feedback, 46–7, 49
Audiometry, 109–14
  not suitable for screening tests in young children, 103
  pure tone, 75, 104, 110–12; Figure VII.6, page 111
  screening tests over 5 years, 103
  speech, 112–14, 125; Figure VII.7, page 113
  with binaural hearing aids, 134–5
Auditory pathway, Figure III.3, page 26
Auditory sensation area, 85–7; Figure VI.1, page 86
Auditory trainer, 137
Auditory training, 7, 116–122; Figure VIII.1, page 119
  definition, 116
  when deafness diagnosed late, 120–1
Auricle, 10, 93, 94
Automatic volume control, 92, 126–7, 130; Figure IX.2 (c), page 126

Babbling, 30–1, 44–9
  by deaf babies, 48–9, 53–4
Backward child, 8, 88
Balance, 13
Békésy, G. von, 16
Bel, 67
Bell, Alexander Graham, 67
Binaural hearing aids, 131–7; Figure IX.3 (b), (c) and (d), page 133
Birds, hearing in, 22–3
Birth injuries, as cause of deafness, 97
Blindness and deafness, 121
Blount, John, 4
"Bonny", the chimpanzee astronaut, 24
Bordley, J. E., analysis of causes of deafness, 89
Brain, its part in hearing, 18–37, 40
Broca's area, 17, 19; Figure III.1 (b), page 19
Burt, Sir Cyril—"The Backward Child", 8

Causes of deafness, 89–98
  anoxia, 97
  birth injuries, 97
  drugs, 93, 97
  kernicterus, 94–6
  meningitis, 97–8
  otitis media, 97
  peri-natal, 90, 94–7
  post-natal, 90, 97–8
  prematurity, 97, 102
  pre-natal, 90–4
  rhesus incompatibility, 95–6, 102
  rubella, maternal, 91–3, 102, 116
  streptomycin, 97
  thalidomide, 93
  wax in external auditory meatus, 97
Cawthorne, Sir Terence, 2, 3
Central deafness, 85, 88–9
Central nervous system, diseases of, as cause of central deafness, 88
Cochlea, 13, 92; Figure II.3, page 14; Figure II.5, page 15
Cochlear nerve, 13
Cochleopalpebral reflex, 25–6; Figure III.4 (a), page 27
Colliculus, inferior, 25; Figure III.3, page 26
Colour blindness, 77
Communication, 11, 21–2, 38–9
Comprehension hearing, 24–5, 116
Conditioned reflex, 23, 34
Conductive deafness, 75, 85–7, 94, 97
Consonants, information supplied by, 43
Coquet, M., 94
Cortex, auditory, 24; Figure III.1 (b), page 19
  cerebral, 17, 18–21, 24, 25; Figure III.1 (a) and (b), page 19; Figure III.3, page 26
  motor, Figure III.1 (b), page 19 Figure III.2, page 20
  sensory, Figure III.1 (b), page 19
Corti, organ of, 13, 92; Figure II.5, page 15; Figure II.6, page 16
Coupland, Phyllis, Figure VII.4, page 107
Crawling, 49
Cues for recognition of speech, 78–81

Day nursery for normally hearing children, valuable, 120, 138
Deaf children in ordinary schools, 6, 7, 8, 121, 138
Deafness, acquired, 84–5, 97–8
  aid clinic, 3, 7
  causes of; see Causes of deafness, 88–98
  central, 85, 88–9
  conductive, 75, 85–7, 94, 97

141

Deafness (*Contd.*)
detection of; *see* Detection of deafness, 99–103
effects of, on learning to hear, 35–6
on speech reception, 74–6
familial, 90
hereditary, 90–1
high tone loss, 87, 96, 127
mixed, 85, 88
perceptive, 75, 85, 87–8, 92, 96
peripheral, 85
sensori-neural; *see* Perceptive deafness
suspicion of, 99–101
total, 35, 130
types of, 84–9
Decibel, 67–9
Deduction in learning of language, 62
Detection of deafness, 99–103
importance of early, 99
in older children, 103
Dictionary, mental, 50–1
Distortion, 75–6, 128
Drugs, as cause of deafness, 93, 97

Ear, the, and how it works, 10–17
diagrammatic section through, Figure II.1, page 10
drum, 11, 22
inner, 13
middle, 11, 12, 22
deformities of, 93–94
outer, 10
deformities of, 93–4
Early detection of deafness, importance of, 99
Electroencephalograph, use of, in audiometry, 104
Endolymph, 13, 15
Environment, importance of, in hearing, 33–4
Ernaud, 8
Erythroblastosis foetalis, 95
Eustachian tube, 11–2; Figure II.4, page 14
External auditory meatus, 10, 11, 93
wax in, as cause of deafness, 97

Facility to learn, special, in early life, 33
Familial deafness, 90
Feedback, auditory, 46–7, 49
Feeling, threshold of, 86
Fenestra ovalis, 13, 15
rotunda, 15
Fenestration, 16
Finger spelling, 1
Fisch, L., 96
Fish, hearing apparatus, 13, 22
Frequencies, high and low in speech, 73–4
Frequency range of hearing aid, 127
response curve of hearing aid, 127
Fry, D. B., analysis of causes of deafness, 89, 90, 92, 95

German measles; *see* Rubella
"Go" Game, the, 107–12; Figure VII.5 page 108; Figure VII.6, page 111
Golden Square Fund, 130
Goldstein, Dr. Max A., 123
Grammar, development of, 60–4
Gregg, N. McA., 91
Griffiths, Ruth—"The abilities of babies", 104
Guessing, importance of, in understanding speech, 40–3; Figure IV.1, page 42

Haemolytic disease of the new born, 95
Hair-cells, 13; Figure II.6, page 16
Hardy, W. G., Analysis of causes of deafness, 89
Health visitors, 102, 103
Hearing aids, 3, 4, 8, 36, 48, 49, 70, 117, 123–37; Figure IX.1, page 124; Figure IX.3, pages 132–3
acoustic gain, 125
amplification, 125
auditory trainer, 137
automatic volume control, 126–7, 130
binaural, 131–37; Figure IX.3 (*b*), (*c*) and (*d*), page 133
body-worn, 131; Figure IX.3 (*a*)(i), page 132; Figure IX.3 (*c*) and (*d*), page 133
bone conduction, 131
characteristics, 123, 125–7
choice of, 130–7
distortion, 128
ear level aid, 131; Figure IX.3 (*a*)(ii), page 132; Figure IX.3 (*b*), page 133
fallacies about, 127–30
fear of acoustic trauma, 128–9
first electrical, 123
frequency range, 127
frequency response curve, 127
function of, 127–8
induction loop system, 137
lip reading, learning of, facilitated, 130
Medresco aid, 4, 130
mechanical, 123; Figure IX.1, page 124
Monopack experiment, 130
output, 125–7
methods of limiting, 126–7
peak clipping, 126
performance, 123
sensitivity, 125
specification, 123
spectacles, 131
tests of hearing with, 109
types of, 131–7
Y-leads, 137
Hearing, comprehension, 24–5, 116
evolution of, 21–3
in animals, 10–11, 21–4
residual, 1, 35, 37, 116

Hearing (*Contd.*)
 tests of, 103–14; *see* Tests of hearing
 usable, 116
Hereditary deafness, 90–1
Homunculus, the motor, Figure III.2, page 20
Hostel, for deaf babies and their mothers, Ealing, 117

Imitation, role of, in speech development, 28, 47, 57; Figure III.6, page 30
Incus, 13; Figure II.2, page 12
Induction loop system, 137
Inhibition of response, 26
Institute of Laryngology and Otology, 4, 5
Intelligence tests, 114–15

Janette, 1
Jefferson, Sir Geoffrey, 5
"Jock of the Bushveld", 120

Kernicterus, as cause of deafness, 94–6

Labyrinth, 13
Lack, David—"The Life of the Robin", 23
Language, development of, 49–53
Learning to hear, 23–37
 conditions for, 36–7
Livingstone, Gavin, 94
Lip reading, 1, 2, 82
 learning of, facilitated, 130
Listening, development of capacity for, 45
Littler, Dr. T. S., 130
Localisation of sound, 136; Figure III.4 (*c*), page 27
London County Council, School Medical Service, 3, 4
Loop systems, 137
Love, Kerr, 34, 36
Lucas, H. A., 97

Malleus, 12–13; Figure II.2, page 12
Manual method, 1
Maturation, 32
Meaning of words, 59–60
Medresco aid, 4, 130
Ménière's disease, 13
Meningitis, as cause of deafness, 5
 meningo-coccal, 97
 tuberculous, 97–8
Mental backwardness, 88, 114, 121
Milestones of development, 32
Ministry of Health, *Memorandum on Services for Young Children Handicapped by Impaired Hearing*, 100
Monopack experiment, 130
Mother, importance of, in speech development, 6–7, 37, 57–8
Multiple handicaps, children with, 121–2
Myelination, 32–3

Neville, Miss Blanche, 2
Normal school, the deaf child in, 6, 7, 8, 121, 138
Nouns, learning of, 63
Nuffield Hearing and Speech Centre, 4
Nuffield pictures, Figure VII.4, page 107

Operator word, 61
Oral method, 1
Ormerod, Frank, 4
Ossicles, auditory, 12–13, 22; Figure II.2, page 12
Otitis media, as cause of deafness, 97
Otosclerosis, 15
Oval window, 13, 15

Partially deaf units, 3, 121, 138
Pavlov, 23, 24
Peak clipping, 126; Figure IX.2 (*b*), page 126
Peet, E. W., 94
Pegg, Mr., 134
Perceptive deafness, 75, 85, 87–8, 92, 96
Perilymph, 13, 15
Petit mal, as cause of central deafness, 88
Phonemes, 41–2, 51–7
Phonemic system, 51–7, 80–1
Pinna, 10
Predictability of sounds, 43
Prematurity, as cause of deafness, 97, 102
Prepositions, learning of, 63
Pronouns, learning of, 64
Psychological testing, 114–15
Psychosis, as cause of central deafness, 88
Pure tone audiometry, 110–12; Figure VII.6, page 111
 using electroencephalograph, 104

Rayners School, 4
Reading, helpful in acquisition of speech, 120, 138
Recognition of words, 56, 78
Recruitment, 88, 92
Redundancy in language, 43–4, 78
Reflex, cochleopalpebral, 25–6; Figure III.4 (*a*), page 27
Reflex, conditioned, 23, 34
Reflex, general acoustic muscle, 25–6; Figure III.4 (*a*), page 27
Reinforcement of conditioned reflex, 34
Residual hearing, 1, 35, 37
Rhesus incompatibility, 95–6, 102
Risk, children at, 102–3
Robin, song, 23
Round window, 15
Royal National Throat, Nose and Ear Hospital, 3
Rubella, deafness due to maternal, 91–3, 102, 116

Scala tympani, Figure II.3, page 14; Figure II.5, page 15
vestibuli, Figure II.3, page 14; Figure II.5, page 15
School, normal, the deaf child in, 121, 138
Screening, tests of hearing, 101–2
Sentence construction, 64
Sign language, 1
Silverman, Dr. Richard, 116
Sound, discrimination of, 78–9
energy, 65–9
in speech sounds, 69–73
infants deprived of, 34–5, 57
infants' responses to, 25–31
localisation of, 28, 136; Figure III.4 (c), page 27
Spastics, 95–6, 121
examination of hearing, 96
Speech, 11, 22
audiometry, 112–14, 125; Figure VII.7, page 113
with binaural hearing aids, 134–5; Figure IX.4, page 135
Speech and language, 39–44
Spontaneous speech, deaf children with, 4–8, 36, 117
Stapedectomy, 16
Stapes, 13, 15; Figure II.2, page 12
Startle response, 25–6; Figure III.4, page 27
Streptomycin, as cause of deafness, 97
Suspicion of deafness, 99–101
Swan, C., et al., 91
Syllables, 54, 70–1

Tervoort, Dr. B. T., on babbling, 30–1

Tests of hearing, 103–14
amateur tests, 101
developmental tests, 104
in spastics, 96
screening tests, 101–3
the "Go Game", 107–9; Figure VII.5, page 108
the older child, 104–9
with hearing aid, 109
Thalidomide, as cause of deafness, 93
Tracy, John Tracy Clinic, Los Angeles, 102
Tracy, Mrs. Louise, 102
Tympanic cavity, 11, 12
membrane, 11
Types of deafness, 84–9

Vaccines for rubella, 93
Verbs, learning of, 63
Vestibular nerve, 17
Vocabulary, active, 50, 59
indexing, 139
passive, 50, 59
Vocal cords, 74
Voice, response to mother's, 28, 30
Vowels, information supplied by, 43

Walker, A. S., 97–8
Watt, 66
Whetnall, Edith, 89, 90, 92, 95, 97
Wishart, Dr., 116
Words, 58–60

Xylophone, for tests of hearing, 109

Y-leads, 137
Yearsley, M., analysis of causes of deafness, 89, 90
Young, John, 4